Across the Footbridge
By Martha Jons'

Cover Design and Illustration by Michael Beezley

ISBN 0-9676373-0-9 9.95

This book is based on my memories of my mother's life. Other's shared in these events with me and their own recollections may vary from mine. This is my personal tribute to my mother and the many others that suffer as she did.

Special thanks go out to all of the people who helped make this book a reality.

To Ruth, who without your encouraging edits, *and more edits*, and the many hours you spent assisting me with the painful task of logging my memories into a readable form, this book would not have been possible.

To Liphee, my surrogate mother and one of my dearest friends, thank you for then and now.

To Michael and Jennifer, the two children that I gave birth to and the wonderful adults that you grew to become.

To Bill, who found the child inside of me and led her out of the darkness and into the sunlight, forever and a day.

To the many whom God has brought into my life, not to replace, but for me to appreciate because of others taken from me.

To Rabbit from Hopsing.

Chapter One

1:40 am, Sunday, April 3, 1971

"Somebody'd better have the dispatcher give the coroner a call... an' tell em' to cancel the diver. I think we've got her! See if some of the family can come over here and identify the body. Better make sure it's the one we've been lookin' for."

The men's faces were caught and frozen for a split second with each rotation of the blue and white lights.

The **Daily News** responded to the tragic death with a four-paragraph obituary on page five. Along with the

1

appropriate dates and names of survivors, the article gave an explanation as to the cause of death, or did it?

...

June3, 1954

The water collecting at the basin where the two hills come together would eventually find its way into the Gulf of Mexico. In some places it was little more than a small trickle before growing again in width as it traveled east increasing in size with each mile. In the heat of August, the entire stream almost evaporated into the creek bed, leaving small minnows and crawdads scurrying to find water for their survival. After the April rains, the creek swelled into a convulsing monster traveling towards the Ohio River with the determination of a mother bear protecting one of her young. Sometimes, the water came within inches of touching the bottom of the bridge in front of the little house and anyone brave enough to stand on the bridge and look down into the swirling brown rapids could occasionally see parts of other peoples' lives pass underneath. Toys, bits of trash, pop bottles, and homemade toy boats, traveled at the speed of the current, making their way towards a distant ocean. Occasionally a lost doll passed under the bridge, its unblinking eyes staring towards the sky.

By the first week of June the creek that'd just run its yearly marathon was once again returning to a small tributary. The three boys sat on the bridge looking down between dangling bare feet for the last treasures of the year to pass beneath them.

Larry who was four years old with red hair and a blanket of freckles crossing his nose and cheeks turned to the boy on his right.

Across the Footbridge

"How can it hurt that bad?"

Eddie was eight and could recall Roger's, or Rob's as his brothers referred to him, birth a couple of years before but knew that Larry wasn't ready to hear the details. Rob, at two and a half, swallowed back more of the tears he'd been battling with all morning. Eddie looking from one brother to the other stumbled for a response. The boys were sent out to play several hours ago, before Elly arrived. The midwife had patted each boy's head as she passed him on the bridge that connected Pappy's yard with the other side of the creek.

Larry wanted to question her about the bag she carried. He was doubtful that the baby she was bringing was really in her bag because he'd overheard the grown-ups talking about what might happen when the baby did come. And, he couldn't comprehend how a baby in a bag could make his mother scream in agony, before the baby or the midwife arrived. He knew there was more to it than that and thought that maybe Eddie would explain it to him.

Eddie was frightened by the sound of his mother's screams that penetrated the windows and walls of the small frame house and he still remembered the first morning that he found Roger asleep in Pappy's bed. He woke to hear whispers coming from Pappy and Grandma's kitchen and crawled from beneath the heavy quilts and over Larry who was sleeping along side of him, following the voices into the lighted kitchen. There he found three of the five adults that lived in the three-room house. Pappy, his Uncle George, and Aunt Liphee were sitting at the kitchen table. Pappy was the first to notice him.

"Son, come here. You have another brother."

As Charley lifted his grandson onto his lap the sleepy

3

boy leaned towards his warmth. Eddie sensed the tension penetrating the silence that replaced the whispers when he entered the room.

"Where's Mommy?"

"Son, the midwife, Elly, is in with your mother. There was a problem last night; your mother'll need a lot of rest before she'll be feeling better. Just so you'll know and won't be frightened by it, she lost a lot of blood trying to give birth to your new brother. But, he's fine, an' right now he's asleep beside your grandmother. Why don't you go take a peek at him?"

Eddie felt fear start to beat its little drum in his chest.

"Pappy, when can I see my mommy?"

"Soon son, soon."

Eddie left the kitchen and returned to the bedroom. He passed the bed where Larry lay with his little butt protruding into the cold air and a thumb close to his ready mouth. At the other side of the room was the bed where Pappy and Grandma slept. He quietly walked to the bed and placed a hand on his grandmother's face.

"Is that you Eddie?" The blind woman recognized the touch of the small hand.

"Yes Grandma, it's me. Pappy said the baby is a boy."

Maggie eased the covers away from a lump of bedding to reveal a small dark head and two tiny fists.

"Your grandfather said the hair I feel is dark like yours."

Eddie wondered again what it would be like to be blind like his grandmother. Sometimes he blindfolded his eyes to see

4

if he could feel things with his hands and recognize them like she did. He never knew if he recognized the objects from touch or because he saw them before he closed his eyes.

"He does, and his face is fat too. Pappy said I can see my mommy soon."

"I know son, you be good while you wait."

Maggie tucked the blanket over the infant and closed her eyes hoping Eddie would think she'd gone back to sleep and leave the room. He did and left the room as quietly as he entered it. Once she heard his small voice coming from the kitchen, she released the tears she'd been holding back. "Lord," she whispered into the still air, "will he see his mommy soon?"

Mary, Maggie's youngest child, was five years older than Eddie and she was instructed to take him outside after breakfast to distract him while the midwife worked behind the quilt partition that separated him from his mother. Eddie had been out of bed for two hours when Pappy came out and called for Mary to bring him inside. The midwife was leaving through the kitchen door as they went in.

The first thing he noticed was the open doorway leading to the room where his mother was. Someone had removed the quilt. The second thing he saw was the bloodstain on the floor that the quilt had concealed.

Liphee was in the room with his mother when he went to stand at the side of her bed. His eyes grew large with fear as he blinked at the tears forming under his lids.

"What's a matter with Mommy's face?"

Turning him towards the door, she nudged him back into the kitchen before answering.

"Honey, Mommy had a stroke last night after your

5

brother was born but she's gonna' be all right. She just needs to rest awhile."

Two years later, Eddy's forehead wrinkled under the strain of remembering Roger's birth and the months that followed. He was the oldest, and had to be brave for the brothers that he was supposed to keep occupied though he probably had more fear for what was happening inside Pappy's house than the other two had combined. He was trying to decide how much of his knowledge he should share with Larry when all three boys heard a familiar whistle. Their heads turned in unison towards the front porch of Pappy's house.

Ben Rice removed his fingers from his mouth when he caught sight of the boys. The whistle signaled them to come now, the same, signaled them to come for supper, come in for the night, or come help carry in coal and water. This time the whistle brought them fast.

"Would you boys like to see your little sister?"

This time there was no blood visible when Eddie stood beside his grandmother's bed looking at another tiny head and two small fists. The three boys peered over their grandmother's shoulder for a glimpse of the baby on the other side. Maggie, exhausted, but relieved that the birth was behind them, had sent her thanks skyward just moments before. Along with her gratitude, she requested that no more babies be lain at her side at the expense of her oldest daughter.

It was June 3, 1954, two and a half years since Roger was born, years filled with the events that led Charley and Maggie to the little red house where Peggy Ann was born. Charley stood at the bedside of his blind wife and looked down at his small granddaughter. This would be the last time he had to suffer this agony for another child being brought into the family. Ginny could not bear any more children. He made this silent promise to himself as he stood on knees that were weakened from the fear of what lay in front of them.

When he did speak his voice was barely audible.

"Mag, she can't go through this again. We can't go through it again."

They'd been together thirty-three years and she felt the same fear. She whispered the only reply that she could accept herself.

"Charley, this time she'll be okay."

With a last look at the sleeping infant he turned and left the room. His words lingered in the air after he walked out of the bedroom, out of the house.

"I hope you are right Mag. This time I pray that you're right!"

The four-room house was one of several set at the base of the hills that enclosed the outskirts of a town in Eastern Kentucky. At the northern side, the town's streets stopped at the railroad tracks that ran parallel with the Ohio River. As the town grew, it expanded in three directions and would eventually consume the hills. Charley Sexton had lived in the area all of his life as had his father and grandfather.

Maggie had lived in and around Lima, Ohio till the day they wed. Fear for the future drove Charley's thoughts back to their wedding day, and his life before that.

'1921'

Mag was his second wife. Rachael was his first wife,

7

the greatest love of his life, and his greatest heartbreak. He married her when he was just a boy, barely sixteen, and at eighteen he was a widower and father of a toddler and an infant. His ma and pa were each holding a grandson in their arms when the doctor quietly informed them that his Rachael was gone. He thought that surely he too would die. Not even a young man as strong as he was could survive the pain that the doctor's words created in his heart. He didn't die as he had often wished and he was left with two small sons.

Ma and Pa were both old and Ma was blind so when he married Rachael she moved in instead of him moving out. After the week of Rachael's death, he left Ma and Pa's house each morning at daybreak to walk to the coal mines where he angrily swung his pick at the elements that had destroyed his young life without the courtesy of killing him first. Each evening he returned home to eat his dinner then fall exhausted into the bed that still held the essence of his wife.

When Rachael had been gone four months, his oldest son had his second birthday. The baby was six months old and Charley felt as if he had the weight of the world riding on his shoulders, each day seeming to hold the time of eternity within its hours.

Pa waited for the right time to approach his son. The right time hadn't presented itself and he knew that it never would. On the day his grandson turned two years old he asked Charley to take a walk with him after supper. The old man had to tell him something that would break both of their hearts, and hopefully save the lives of his grandsons. Pa followed him as they made their way to the back of the house to sit on stumps that had at one time been trees but were now walls of the old house.

"Son, I don't know an easy way to say this." He began
as he placed his arm around the shoulders of the boy who was
to him little more than a child.

"Your mother and I were too old to have kids when the
Good Lord saw fit to place you in our home. At the time we
asked that he let us live to see you into your manhood, and he
did. We didn't ask for more than that because we didn't know
there'd be a need. But there is and we're both old now, and
your mother's blind. We've got two babies to raise... and we
need help. Son, you're gonna have to take another wife."

Pa watched as the reality of his words shattered his
only son.

"Charley." His voice was as gentle as it was when
Charley was a boy riding in front of him on the old mare that
used to carry them to church.

"Son, you'll never find another Rachael but you do
have to find a mother for her sons."

He barely heard the words his son uttered before the
sobs that Charley'd held back for six months took control of
him.

"I know Pa!"

A few weeks after their talk, Charley left the house at
dawn on a Saturday morning. Instead of his work clothes he
wore his church clothes and when he reached the mouth of the
holler he walked towards the bus stop instead of the direction
of the mines. Three hours later a bus stopped at a small town
in Ohio and he got off. He spent the afternoon in the
company of a young woman he'd been introduced to through

the letters of mutual friends. In the late afternoon, he boarded the bus to return home.

Maggie Mosley had spent the afternoon with the man that she would soon marry and her family was not happy that she was marrying a man who had been married before. Her family was not happy that she would soon be rearing children she hadn't given birth to. The fact that she was leaving a comfortable lifestyle to follow a stranger into the depths of a holler somewhere in the hills of Eastern Kentucky was more than they would tolerate. She was forbidden to see the miner from Kentucky again.

Three weeks later, Maggie left her parents' home carrying a small bag and dragging a trunk filled with expensive clothes. She boarded a bus headed for a town forty miles south. That afternoon Maggie Mosley became Maggie Sexton in the courthouse of a county that she had never visited before and would never see again.

Charley spent the last money he had on a hotel room and for their wedding supper they ate the food Ma had sent with him that morning. The next day they boarded the bus that took them home to Ma and Pa and Charley's two sons.

Maggie knew Charley wasn't in love with her as he had been with Rachael. She understood and she loved him enough for the two of them, for now.

They lived in the same house with Ma and Pa and on their second anniversary she gave birth to a daughter. For the first time since the day Rachael died, Charley felt that he had a reason to live. They named her Ginny.

Maggie never mentioned the life she'd lived before her marriage and the trunk of expensive clothing remained packed away. The log house Charley took her to the second day of their marriage contained everything she needed; it contained her husband.

The years passed and more babies followed Ginny's birth, a son followed by a daughter, and then another son. Gar and Willie, the sons born to Rachael welcomed each new arrival, Ginny, George, then Liphee and Jesse. The four adults and six kids crowded into the house Pa built years before for him and Ma.

Before the last child was born, Jesse died. Charley placed him alongside Rachael with the knowledge that she would now watch over one of Mag's babies as Mag had watched over hers. Maggie gave birth to another girl the summer that Ginny turned sixteen. They named their last daughter Mary.

Ginny was eighteen when Ma was placed on the other side of Jesse, the same year that she started to withdraw from the family. For a while nobody noticed that she was a little quieter but as the months passed she became more withdrawn and it became apparent to the others that she had changed. In the spring she became obsessed with a small imperfection that appeared on her face. Charley took her to a local doctor who removed the mole. A few months later the blotch returned and Ginny's sole focus became the small blemish that the rest of her family could barely see. As the months passed, Charley watched his daughter become someone unfamiliar. He took her to all of the local doctors but they couldn't tell him why she was as she was…or if she would ever return to herself. Then, as gradually as she had left her family, she returned leaving the fear of what had removed her from them to live in Charley long after she was again restored to her old self. His heart told him that the same force that returned Ginny to him would again return for her.

Ginny was twenty-one when she decided that she wanted to be married. Till then Charley had discouraged every potential boy that had shown an interest in her, his heart continually reminding him of the illness that removed her from him two years before. If the disease returned for her again he wanted to have her in his protective custody.

The man Ginny wanted to marry was nine years older than she was. He'd been married and divorced and he had two children. Those were the reasons her father gave for forbidding the marriage.

As her mother had done before her, Ginny met up with a man at a county courthouse. Moments later, she became someone's wife.

Chapter Two

1943-1945

Two years had passed since Japanese planes dropped the first bomb at Pearl Harbor triggering the historical speech by Franklin Roosevelt and news of the congressional vote declaring that a war existed between the United States of America and the Empire of Japan. The news made its way from coast to coast and into the homes of the rich and poor alike and had been received in the same way in every corner of the country. As a result of one action by a foreign nation, a country built on refugees became totally united.

The wartime years were filled with ration-coupons and

anxious people waiting for news of victory, or news of the death of a loved one. Charley Sexton could relate to the fear of losing a loved one and also to the want of unavailable items. Most of his life had been lived under similar circumstances, except now, everyone he passed held the same look of panic and deprivation, a look he'd grown accustomed to in the prewar years.

It was late autumn of the year 1943. Ben and Ginny cautiously made their way around the deep ruts in the dirt road that still held water from the last rain. They walked into the holler that divided the two hills as the last of the sun's light faded to dusk. Ginny, apprehensive over facing her father for the first time in her twenty-one years, hesitated.

"Ben, do you think Pappy'll turn us away?"

At thirty years of age Ben Rice could feel masculine confidence pumping through his body along with the blood. He turned to his bride with the only answer he knew.

"No, but if he does... we'll go to my folks."

The little house at the end of the dirt road came into sight with the last of the day's light. Inside, someone had placed a kerosene lamp on the table and it chased the darkness into the corners of the kitchen when the newlyweds opened the door. Charley was sitting at the old wooden table as he had been for the last five hours, waiting. Liphee informed him that her sister had eloped, only after she knew it would be to late for him to intervene. Her keeping of the secret was the only wedding present she was able to give Ginny.

Now, Liphee sat at her father's side waiting to see the results of disobedience. She was disappointed when he turned to her and asked her to leave the room.

Across the Footbridge

Ben and Ginny Rice stood side by side as they had stood earlier in the day. Ginny looked into the face of a defeated man when she stood in front of her father the day she took someone else's name. Charley looked from one to the other of the young people as they fidgeted, waiting for his words.

"Ginny, I've valued your life more'n I've ever valued my own, and I've wanted nothing more than to keep'n protect you. But, you've grown up and decided that you now know what's best. I hope you're right in the choice you've made today."

With these words spoken, he turned to the man that yesterday he looked on as a friend.

"Ben, you've been married and divorced an' already fathered two kids of your own. Now, I trust you'll care for Ginny as you'd want someone to care for your own daughter. If the day ever comes that you can't do that, I expect you to return her to me. And remember, if you don't do as I've asked... I'll kill you with my own hands."

Ben swallowed the lump in his throat along with the advice, then reached to shake the hand extended to him.

For five weeks, room was made in the old log house for one more. With the war claiming more of the young men in the area another property soon became available and Ben and Ginny moved into a three-room house with white siding about two miles from the home where she grew up. Ben drove a dump truck hauling the coal from the base of the mines to the dock on the Ohio River. Charley and Ginny's brother, George, were two of the miners that dug the coal out of the sides of the hills. Gar and Willie, Charley's sons by Rachael,

15

left Kentucky soon after the war started and they were somewhere fighting for the freedom of their families and the future of the children they hoped to have.

Ben and Ginny settled into their first home but the two boys that he fathered in his previous marriage never became a part of their lives. They continued to live with the relatives that he placed them with after his divorce and within weeks of their wedding Ginny was pregnant with their first child and her husband's age became something to be grateful for. The war in Europe was winding down and his number had never been called by the draft lottery.

Each morning, Ginny rose before the sun to build a fire in the small coal stove in her tiny kitchen. She'd cook their breakfast and heat water for Ben to shave with before he began to stir. Later, she'd stand at the kitchen door where he kissed her before he left to go to the mines. As the months passed, the baby growing inside her placed distance between the young couple's shadow falling across the kitchen floor. It'd been decided that the last weeks of her pregnancy would be spent under her father's roof.

Maggie Mosley-Sexton 1921-1943

The years that'd passed since Maggie Mosley became Maggie Sexton had brought about many changes. The first day Charley led Maggie into the three-room house she wasn't sure what kind of reception she would receive. The year was 1921. In Lima, Ohio where she'd been born and brought up, people similar to her parents had surrounded her. All of her life, the people in it had been comfortable and everything they had needed had always been available before the need for it arose.

Maggie's first indication that her needs would be changing came with the long walk from the isolated country road where the bus deposited her and Charley to the small house she was to share with her in-laws. She was tired and her fashionable shoes and stockings were not the standard walking attire of this area of Kentucky. After she'd stumbled over the deep ruts in the dirt road several times, he set the burden of her large trunk down in the middle of the road that was little more than a widened path.

"Mag, don't you want to change your shoes to something a little more practical?"

A bride of one day, she straightened her shoulders before she again started walking towards the direction he'd earlier pointed her. Her words carried back over her shoulder to answer the first question he'd asked her that day.

"I want to get to my new home in time to help your ma with dinner. I don't have time to rummage through that whole trunk in order to find old shoes to put on my young feet."

She didn't know how to tell him that the shoes she was wearing were the oldest and most comfortable ones she owned. What in the world would she ever do with a trunk filled with expensive finery? This question repeatedly crossed her mind as her husband again shouldered the heavy burden of her wardrobe and they walked the remaining mile that separated them from her new home.

Maggie's first view of the house could have been a page removed from a scenic calendar. The little log house set snuggled into the adjoining curve of the two hills she and

Charley had just walked between. The rough boards of the front porch had weathered to a pewter gray and to the right of the front door set a rocking chair stirring in the evening breeze. Blue smoke curled up from a rock chimney protruding from the handmade shingles of the slanted roof. The spaces between the logs had been filled with the red clay she'd first seen when they walked along the creek flowing at the other end of the holler. They stopped in front of the house and she could sense his relief. He turned to face her before leading her inside to introduce her to a ready-made family.

"Mag, it ain't much an' its a lot less than you been used too, but Pa built it all with his own two hands."

The first thing she saw when Charley opened the door leading into the kitchen was two faces stair stepping up from a hand-hewn table. The baby was sitting on his grandmother's knee. In his fat fists he clutched the metal ring of a Mason jar, drools connecting the ring to a toothless mouth. Standing close to the knee that held the baby was a little boy about two years old. His eyes took in Maggie with a look of maturity that belied his age and frightened her a little. Both children silently watched Charley remove Maggie's coat from her shoulders then call out to the other rooms of the house.

"Pa, We're home."

Ma remained seated at the table till Charley closed the distance that separated them and his large hands easily plucked his son from her lap. By the time Pa found his way into the kitchen Ma had made her way to Maggie's side. Standing in front of her son's wife, who she would never see, she leaned a little closer to whisper her first words of welcome. "He still hasn't figured out that my hearing didn't go when my sight did."

Ma and Pa accepted Maggie as the answer to the many prayers they'd prayed and her first week as a new bride and mother was eased by the gentle kindness they placed around her. Willie and Gar continued to cling to the familiar knees of their grandmother.

Maggie's smooth hands became rough with their introduction to cold well water and lye soap. She soon became accustomed to the routine that'd been established many years before. Ma, with the help of Pa, had maintained the little house and the care of two infants without the aid of being able to see what she was doing. Maggie was always careful to replace things in the exact spot where she found them and Ma and Pa relaxed with the knowledge that Maggie was quick enough to rescue Gar from the pitfalls a two-year-old manages to find.

Charley carried in coal and water and carried out the ashes before he left the house each day to go to the mines. Ma instructed Maggie in the upkeep of the small house. She learned to prepare a meal with little more than an empty pot and soon could bank the fire in the old cast-iron stove at night as well as her husband. She would rise before the chickens and stir the still warm embers into a flame. When spring came, she planted her first taters. When fall came, Ma showed her how to preserve the food she'd grown. By the time she was sure that she was carrying the seed of her firstborn, she could barely recall the life she'd once lived under the shelter of her father's roof.

The years passed and the walls of the little house seemed to bulge from the growth of more children. One by one, Maggie brought out a dress or a pair of shoes from the trunk Charley carried up the holler so many years before. Occasionally, a new dress was torn into scrap pieces to make into a curtain to replace a wooden shutter. Sometimes a piece of silk was sewn into the faded knee of a pair of over-alls. Never once did Maggie open her trunk with regret for her lack of means. She had the one thing that she needed most. She had Charley.

By the time Ma was placed beside Charley's first wife, Maggie's eyesight had started to fade. At first it seemed as if the clouds of a winter storm had forgotten to take their leave with the arrival of the bright sunshine and she soon learned to make the most of sunny days. The faces of her children became fuzzy to her in the years that followed. As her mother-in-law before her had done, Maggie gradually lost her vision. Her last daughter's newborn face was a blur of pink skin that continued to fade with the years that followed.

After Ma's death, Pa took up residence in the old rocker that still set at the side of the front door. His grandchildren became adults in the space of time that he rocked and waited. His hair became snow white with this passage of time and his long white beard cascaded down from his face leaving his nose and eyes as the only bits of color standing out against the white. Being an old man when he fathered Charley, his age became something that through the years his grandchildren speculated about. Years came and went as he rocked away the time remaining before he could join his wife in eternity.

Maggie's   acceptance   of   the   poverty   Charley

introduced her to was typical of the woman that she remained. During the weeks that he earned little to accommodate the needs of his family, Maggie's cheerful nature remained. One by one she'd borne his children and year after year she'd worked to stretch his meager earnings to cover the needs of their family. The kind of joy that Charley found in his children, Maggie found in him. She never once questioned the misplacement of his devotion. His children were first in his heart. He was first in hers.

1945

The years of hard work and worry had taken a toll on the young man who went to Ohio to find and return with a mother for his two young sons. By the time Ginny and Ben returned to his door as man and wife, Charley Sexton had accepted the fact that his only riches lay in his children.

Gar and Willie were off fighting a war. His other living son had grown to resemble a man in stature but still had the emotions and mentality of a boy caught somewhere between the two worlds. George worked along side him each day in the damp gloom of the mines then returned home in the evenings to chase after and torment his sisters as if he were still a boy of twelve instead of a man of almost twenty.

Liphee, his middle girl, seemed to be more her mother's daughter than the other two. Physically, she resembled the family in Ohio that she'd never seen, her hair coloring and eyes reminding him of Mag all those years ago. Liphee was the independent one and at the age of twelve the strength that she'd eventually grow into was already evident in her.

Across the Footbridge

Mary, the little girl that'd happened along after he and Mag had almost given up the notion of being husband and wife in the true sense of the word, was five years old. An old man with a young girl to rear, what'd he been thinking when he created that one? Short and chubby with black curls growing down her back, she was his last baby. He had asked for enough years to see her grown.

Ginny was expecting her first child in a few weeks. The same love that'd kept him up nights rocking his children through bouts of childhood illnesses now told him that he should have asked for more time. The joy that should've filled his heart with the prospect of welcoming a new generation, was instead a heavy burden of premonition that the future held grief for his firstborn daughter and the life that she was carrying. All of his years of hard work had barely enabled him to keep enough food on his table to keep his family fed. All of his worry never prevented life from taking the course that it wanted, instead of the one he would've preferred.

September, 1945

Ben and Ginny moved back in with Pappy the last week of September to wait for the arrival of the baby. Ginny's belly had grown through the summer to hide the sight of her toes as they become too swollen for her shoes to accommodate them. She spent the better part of the summer readying things for the baby. Muslin had been bleached to a snowy white before she cut and hemmed it into diapers. Yards of flannel had been made into gowns and blankets.

Everything was waiting for her to return to the little house that she'd turned into her and Ben's first home. The privacy the couple gave up in order for her to be close to her family was replaced with the security of knowing that she wouldn't be alone when her labor started.

In the early hours of October 12, 1945, Ginny's water broke. Charley and Ben were sent to bring the mid-wife. Ginny's labor was long and hard, her screams of agony radiating through the small house to carry a distance down the holler. By late afternoon a baby boy was nursing at her breast. When he gave his first angry squalls at his exposure to the world everyone present agreed that he'd been worth the pain and his mother soon forgot the anguish of the hours of labor pain she endured bringing him into the world.

Charley Sexton and Benjamin Rice stood side by side looking down at the child that would carry both of their names. Benjamin Edward Rice came into the world on Columbus Day, 1945.

When Eddie was six weeks old Ginny and Ben returned with him to their own home. Each day that Ben went to the mines Ginny bundled up her son in the late morning hours and with his dirty diapers tucked in a wagon beside him they went to Pappy's. Once there, Liphee and Mag helped her scrub the diapers on a wash board and hang them on a line to dry. In the afternoon the diapers were removed from the line and folded and Ginny placed the baby in the wagon with the clean diapers and returned home to prepare supper.

Chapter Three

Liphee, who turned thirteen at the end of September, was frightened by the sounds coming from the house the day that Eddie was born. She could barely remember Mary's birth five years before. She'd been sent to a neighbor's house for the night and returned the following day to find her sister sleeping by her mother's side. Her nephew's birth she remained home for.

She'd taken Mary outside to occupy her during the hours the mid-wife spent in the bedroom with Ginny. The sounds coming from the house that day scared her as much as Mary. After what seemed to her to be an eternity both girls were summonsed to come meet their nephew. Ginny had been resting with a baby tucked under the covers. Three months later, the sounds of that day were beginning to fade from Liphee's memory.

In the weeks following Eddie's birth the entire family had surrendered themselves to him and each day he was admired anew. He left a large void in their lives when he returned to his home with Ginny and Ben

On a cold January day Maggie sent Liphee to Ginny's house to see that all was well with the baby. It was noon and Ginny hadn't appeared at her mother's house as she'd done in the days since she'd returned home.

Liphee skipped over the ruts in the dirt road, making a game out of which rocks to avoid, on her walk to her sister's house. She was caught in the space of transition between the little girl she'd been and the young woman her body was leading her towards. Caught between the two worlds, at times she wanted to cling to the security of her childhood while moments later she was filled with desires for her future. She appeared to be in no hurry to make the transition that her body was taking her through. She dawdled along the isolated country road that morning, occasionally stopping to watch the steam her breathing made in the chilled air.

When she was in sight of Ginny's house she noticed that no smoke was rising from the chimney. There should've been a fire in the stove for heat, especially with a baby in the house. Ginny's house consisted of three rooms connected by two open doorways. The house had a small porch sheltering its front door and at the back another door opened into the kitchen. It was the back door Liphee knocked at, calling her

25

sister's name. When there was no response, she pushed open the door and entered the small room.

The chilled air in the kitchen told her that no fuel had been placed in the stove for several hours, and with it past noon, she knew that Ben had been at work for almost six hours. The sight of the breakfast dishes on the table told a story of their own. Ginny took a great deal of pride in the house she'd turned into her and Ben's first home and she would never leave her chores undone. Liphee took in the scene before her, feeling fear start to take root somewhere in the bottom of her stomach. She walked into the adjoining room, unaware that each step would take her further into her adult life.

Ginny was crouched at the foot of the iron bed, her hands clutching the spokes of the bed frame. Within her reach, was the ax that Ben used to split the wood he started the fires in the coal stoves with. Instantly, Liphee's eyes darted about the room, searching for her nephew. No baby in the room, she strained to hear sounds coming from the other room, sounds that a baby should make. As she took in the scene before her, Ginny seemed oblivious to her presence.

Fear continued to grow in her till her chest walls begged to explode from the force. Her heart beat faster and faster till she could hear her blood rushing past her ears. With a strength that hadn't existed moments earlier, she forced herself to walk the few steps that'd take into the remaining room, the one containing her nephew's crib. The seconds those few steps consumed became endless, making time, as she had known before, meaningless. With the crib within her sight, she expelled the breath she'd inhaled moments before. The baby

Across the Footbridge

was sleeping with the covers tucked around him from when his mother placed him there hours before. Liphee returned to her sister's side.

Ginny still showed no awareness to her surroundings. Liphee shook her, repeatedly calling her name. She tried for what seemed to her was hours to pry Ginny's hands loose from the bed. She failed. Ginny's grip on the spokes of the bed was so tight that it left her fingers colorless. She'd held them in one position for hours.

Once she realized that she couldn't do anything for her sister by herself, Liphee bundled the baby and returned with him to her mother. She ran, with tears blinding her vision, stumbling over the same rocks that she'd carefully avoided moments before. She found her way to the back door of her home, a door that'd never hold the security for her it had an hour before.

Maggie struggled in her effort to calm Liphee enough to find out what was wrong. Once she stopped sobbing enough to relay the situation, Maggie sent her to the closest neighbor for help. The neighbor went to get assistance while Liphee returned to the cold bedroom to sit by Ginny's side.

A few miles away, seven men sat at the entrance of a hole they'd tunneled into the side of a hill. With their backs turned against the winter wind, they huddled together in a small circle sharing news of the war and eating the food they removed from their lunch pails, their hard hats resting against their feet. The sound of the vehicle made each man set his lunch on the ground and rise to see who was approaching the mine. Charley recognized his neighbor's truck before it came to an abrupt stop a few feet from where the men stood. The fear he'd carried in his heart for years became a reality. Within two minutes, he and Ben were on their way to Ginny, both afraid of what they would find when they got there.

The truck braked to a stop a few feet from the little porch. Liphee turned to look up at the three men who stood looking down at her and her sister. With her father looking into her eyes, she spoke words that tore through his heart as if a bullet had been fired at him at close range.

"Pappy, She's gone!"

Ben watched the scene before him as if it were a movie he'd once seen at the theatre in town. The woman crouched at the foot of the old iron bed held no resemblance to the wife he'd left earlier that day. The ax he left at the side of the kitchen door the night before was inches away from her hands. The imagined possibilities of what could've happened drained the color from his face. Liphee saw his gaze move from the ax to the direction of the room containing his son's crib and recognized his thoughts. She left her sister's side and went to him.

"Ben, Eddie is safe. I took him to Mommy before I went for help."

It took three men to loosen Ginny's hands from their grip on the bed where her son was conceived. Once her hands were freed, she became as docile as a sleeping child and allowed her father to lead her away from her home and take her to his. Ben helped place his wife in the neighbor's truck then went back inside his house to secure the kitchen door. On his way out his eyes again took in the sight of the ax leaning against the foot of the bed. He felt a chill move through his body and squeezed his eyes shut against the flow of tears before he climbed into the back of the truck with Liphee.

After Ginny was placed in her parents' bed, a conversation was held between her husband and father. The two men walked from the bed where she lay into the kitchen, both filled with fear and concern. The last two hours had disrupted the life that Ben felt secure about. He stood facing Ginny's father, unsure of what to say or how to say it. He removed his hard miner's hat and fiddled with the carbide light that was still attached to it. He apparently put his hat back on in his rush to get to his wife. He cleared his throat, walked to the kitchen door, opened it and spat. He closed the door and turned to face Charley.

"Maybe we should see about taking her to that place at the other end of the state."

At five feet ten inches tall, Ben Rice had to tilt his head to meet the eyes of his father-in-law who stood six feet four inches in his stocking feet. Ben could see his words penetrate Charley's heart. The big man made one statement before he turned to leave the room.

"No! We'll keep her here an' we'll take care of her ourselves."

The kitchen door banged shut behind him. He walked around the house to stand beside the remains of the old stump where Pa had his talk with him so many years before. The pain he'd felt then was nothing compared to the excruciating jolts racking his body this time. There was no father sitting at his side when his sobs broke loose. He stood leaning into the back wall of the old house for more than an hour. When his emotions were under control again he braced himself for whatever was in front of them and returned to his daughter's side.

When the winter's sunlight dropped behind the hills the family still seemed to be sleepwalking, waiting for someone to wake them from the nightmare that'd taken control of their lives. In the late afternoon, Liphee returned with Ben to get the essentials they'd need for the baby. Ben wouldn't live long enough to forget the scene of his mother-in-law holding his son to his wife's breast. Her body continued to supply milk for a baby that she was unaware she'd given birth to. He felt as if he'd aged three decades in as many hours. The walk back to Pappy's in the early evening darkness seemed too short. Twelve hours before he kissed his wife at his backdoor and left for work, sure that she'd be there when he returned for supper. His life had been turned upside down in a matter of a few hours' time. Would it right itself again? When would his wife return to him? Would she return?

In the hours following his conversation with Ginny's father, Ben made several trips to the bed where she lay staring at some invisible object he couldn't see. The feelings that overcame him that afternoon had been numerous. Once the shock of seeing her in the condition she was in wore away, questions of what had possibly caused it tumbled through his head. One by one, the questions had been answered. There was no evidence that an intruder had invaded his home, as he first suspected. Ginny's body hadn't been violated in any way that they could tell. The only visible difference in her appearance were milk stains on her dress telling of the morning nursing the baby missed. Had he awakened from his nap to cry himself back to sleep with his mother in the next room? His mind continued to return to an image of the ax leaning

against the end of the bed. He shuttered each time he thought
of what Liphee could've found.

Before Ben and Liphee opened the kitchen door on
their return, he turned to the young girl who'd remained silent
throughout the afternoon.

"Liphee, are you all right?"

Without the youth she possessed hours before, she
replied with the only truth she was sure of.

"No I'm not all right. I'll probably never be all right
again!"

Arrangements for sleeping in the over-crowded house
were juggled, the chance of Ginny walking out the door in the
middle of the night eliminated. The house was quiet long
before the last person fell asleep. Everyone lay awake long
into the night, each person trying to understand what'd taken
place that day. Each heart longed to wake with the morning
light to find the day they'd just lived through was a bad dream.
During the night, Liphee quietly rose from the bed she made
on the floor of her parents' room. Twice before it was time for
the rest of the family to start their day, she changed her
nephew's wet diaper before she held him to his mother. Tears
rolled uncontrolled down her cheeks to dampen the little head
nuzzling at his mother's breast.

The family struggled through the days that followed.
Ginny's father and husband spent most of the first week
taking her to doctors; x-rays were taken, no answers given.
There was no evidence of a brain tumor, no indication of a
virus. There was a baby to be cared for.

The responsibility of Eddie's care fell to Liphee.
Maggie's vision had deteriorated to the point that she could

only detect light from darkness. When the men returned to work, Liphee's eyes watched Ginny through the long winter days. It was Liphee who changed her nephew's diapers and gave him his baths. The hands that held him to his mother's breast were filled with love for the baby who had lost his mother.

As days faded into weeks, Ben realized that he wasn't going to awaken from the nightmare. At times it seemed that he saw a bit of recognition in Ginny's eyes. If he did, it was fleeting. She would eat if food that was placed in front of her but she appeared indifferent to what she ate, or if, displaying no emotions as if someone had disconnected her body from its personality. After two weeks, he closed up the little house and moved the rest of their things into Pappy's. More permanent sleeping arrangements were made. Once again, Ben and Ginny shared the same bed.

With little vision left, Maggie still managed to do a lot of the chores required around the crowded house. These she accomplished by touch and memory as she had witnessed M a do years before. One of the things she couldn't do was see if Ginny walked out a door. In the months following the incident with the bed, this happened several times. Sometimes she was missing for hours, the family searching, calling her name. As quietly as she disappeared, she would return. No one knew where she went the times she silently slipped away. The stress of her disappearances and the fear of her being injured in the state she was in were constant sources of worry to the rest of the family.

Liphee became her sister's constant companion taking her with her when she went to the clothesline to hang up or

Across the Footbridge

take down laundry. She took Ginny to the well to draw water and to the outhouse when nature called. Most of the time she had a baby in her arms or her sister's hand held in hers. The following September, Liphee turned fourteen and her childhood seemed to have happened lifetimes before.

As Eddie grew to be a toddler the absence of his mother went unnoticed to him because of the family that surrounded him. Once his small legs became sturdy and mobile, he tagged after the one closest to him in age and he became Mary's shadow. By his second birthday his mother was expecting another baby. Before Ginny returned to her family, her husband planted the seed of another baby inside her. The news of this impending birth was not as joyously received, as the news of her first pregnancy, and the family became aware of her condition only after her waist expanded and her breasts grew large and heavy. She gradually returned to her family in the last months of her pregnancy. Benjamin Edward Rice celebrated his second birthday October 12, 1948. The first week of December, the mid-wife was again summonsed to the little house in the head of the holler.

Charley and Mag's conversations became limited to the condition of their oldest daughter and their concerns for her future. The illness that destroyed his daughter's home was a constant reminder to Charley of the fears that he'd discussed with her years before. At that time he'd failed to make Mag understand the fear that caused him to want to keep Ginny home with them instead of wanting her to marry and raise a family of her own. By the time he had no need to explain, Ginny's life was disrupted and he struggled with the burden of guilt he continued to carry. Mag continuously reminded him that Ginny had eloped and lectured that at the time no one knew what the future had held for her. Her last argument was the only one he could grasp. Without Ginny and Ben's marriage, Eddie would've never been born.

The years they shared with their grandson were the only two years of their marriage that they had both loved the same. A little boy with black curls and big brown eyes had become the one common denominator that kept them both from losing the battles life continued to pit them against. The mines that'd provided their meager existence unexpectedly closed. Without the coal that Charley and George dug from the hills, there was no need for the truck that Ben drove to make its daily deliveries to the dock at the river. They all lost their jobs the same day. Charley and Mag lay awake long into the nights, discussing how they would possibly keep everyone fed. Before Ginny regained her health to care for the child she had, she would give birth to another. Each morning, Charley Sexton promised himself a better day, a promise that gave him the courage to rise and face what lay in front of him.

The three men spent their first week of being unemployed searching for available work. Without success, they faced reality; if they were going to keep everyone fed they would have to leave the area. Charlie and Ben left the holler on a cold November morning, driving the one vehicle the family had come to rely on two hours north into Ohio. They both started to work the following morning. Ginny was eight months pregnant and easier to manage than she'd been in two years. Most days she was aware of her surroundings and had begun to help with the daily care of her son again. George remained at home to help with the carrying of coal and water.

Across the Footbridge

Hopefully, the men could return home each weekend and with luck the baby would arrive while they were at home.

The illness that laid its claim to Ginny two years before took from a family already weak from their struggle to survive in the poverty of the hills of Kentucky. The small joys that were a part of their existence before had eroded away in those years. Pa had been placed along side his wife the winter before, his last days spent by Ginny's side. Each member of her family would carry the personal scars of an illness that quietly stole into their midst's.

It was a cold Saturday morning in early December, the men returned from Ohio the night before, when Liphee awakened to sounds coming from Ginny and Ben's bed. At first she thought her sister was dreaming. The cold air circulating around her ears and nose told her no one else was out of bed yet so she burrowed deeper under the quilts and was almost asleep again when she heard the same noise coming from the other bed. Instantly, awareness of what was happening brought her to full consciousness. She hurriedly left the warmth of her bed and went to start a fire in the coal stove before summonsing her father. She held a lit match to a few sticks of kindling, quickly placing a handful of coal on top of the flames. Before waking her father and mother, she went to the bed where Ginny lay beside her sleeping husband.

"Ginny, do you know how long you've been in labor?"

Her pupils were clouded with pain when they met Liphee's gaze.

"I don't know for sure. The bed is wet so my water must've broke."

Liphee set the coffeepot on top of the stove, threw

35

more coal on the fire and went to wake her father.

"Pappy, get up, the baby's almost here!"

Minutes later Charley and Ben were headed towards the highway that would take them to Elly's house. Maggie kept Mary and Eddie in the kitchen with George while Liphee stayed at her sister's side waiting for the mid-wife to come. The top of the baby's head had just appeared when she heard the crunch of tires outside the house. At sixteen, Liphee felt that she already had the responsibility of one child on her shoulders. Fifteen minutes later, her niece was placed in her waiting arms. When Liphee looked down at the new life the pain of the last two years melted away and she knew that she was holding one of God's angels.

It had been almost an hour since Mary and Eddie heard the baby cry on the other side of the quilt but they were still confined to the kitchen while the rest of the family took turns going into the room where the baby was. Finally, Pappy reached up and removed the quilt. With the first smile Mary had seen on his face in months, he turned to the only two people in the house who still hadn't met the new arrival.

"Who would like to meet Brenda Sue?"

Mary stood on her toes and Pappy lifted Eddie to the same height for their first look at the baby. She was a little doll that could open and close her eyes, eyes that were bright blue like the sky in June. She had hair so red that Pappy said it would bleed if you broke a strand of it. Eddie would now be Pappy's little man because Brenda Sue would be the baby.

A small baby brought life into the old house. Ginny remained alert after the birth, and held her daughter to her own breast. The entire family rerouted their paths through the house as everyone found reasons to pass the infant that rarely cried.

On Monday, the men returned to their jobs in Ohio. For the first time in two years everyone in the family started to look forward. Maybe by spring, Ben and Ginny could establish a home again. Each weekend the men returned home to find Ginny caring for her daughter herself.

When Brenda was four weeks old she refused the breast her mother offered her. It was Sunday and the men were ready to return to Ohio. Ben offered his finger to his daughter and Brenda caught it in her fist. He laughed at the strength it took to convince her to release her grip. She appeared several months old in size and alertness instead of one month.

Chapter Four

Ben watched Ginny's image standing in the doorway of the old house till she disappeared from the rear-view mirror with the curve of the road. For the first time in almost two years he'd be eager to return home. He'd fathered three sons before Brenda Sue, but her birth touched him in a different way. He had carried guilt inside him like a hidden abscessed sore all of the months that Ginny carried her. Once the rest of the family discovered that Ginny was pregnant, they had each looked at him with accusing eyes. He'd cursed himself more

Across the Footbridge

times than they had, then Brenda Sue emerged from her mother's body. Anyone who looked at her could see she was a blessing. The image of his little girl brought an instant grin to the face that'd almost forgotten how to smile.

Charley looked at him from the other side of the truck seat. With one sentence, he erased the tension that'd lingered between the two men for the past five months.

"Ben, I wished I'd known that Ginny was carrying an angel... maybe then I'd have been easier to live with these last few months."

Ben swallowed at the lump forming in his throat.

"Pappy, I know what you've thought the last few months, an' you was right in your thinking. I didn't think I had the right to get Ginny pregnant either, until I saw the baby. Once I saw her, I was glad I did."

The short conversation eased the tension that'd put distance between the two men. Ten miles later, they were planning their trip home the following weekend.

Ginny watched the steam the old truck expelled from its exhaust pipe evaporate into the winter wind before she closed the front door and returned to the kitchen.

The old house looked drab in the dim winter light with its walls covered with newspaper print. Each spring, clean newspapers were pasted to the walls to cover the smoke of the winter fires. Ginny thought about the many years of papers layered onto the walls. It would help the long winter days pass if the people left in the house could read the print on them. Ben and her father were the only people in the family who could read and write. Education had never been discussed until recently. A letter had arrived the month before addressed to Mr. and Mrs. Sexton. When Pappy returned on Friday night, he read the letter and informed Mary that she'd soon start her schooling.

Ginny passed the two beds that were now a permanent fixture in her mother's front room. The bright remnants of Maggie's long ago dresses had faded with time, blending into the faded denim squares making up the top layers of the quilts that covered both beds. The two beds, Pa's old rocker, and the iron stove were the only furniture the room contained. The other bedroom contained two more beds, a broomstick that Pappy nailed into one of the corners to hang the coats on in the summer and one big chest-of-drawers that held clothes for the entire family. The chest was sufficient since no one ever owned more than three outfits of clothes. Maggie's trunk lid had been converted into a bed for Eddie two years before and the bottom of the trunk held the quilts in the summer.

Ginny walked into the kitchen to sit with the rest of her family. The iron cookstove was older than she was. Pa had built the table before Pappy was born, its top holding the scars of three generations of teething and dings from Mason jar lids. The old icebox was used for dry storage in the winters and some of the summers when money for ice was unavailable. Cold food was stored outside in the winters and hung in the well in summers. The old cupboard holding the dishes and three wooden chairs were the only store-bought-furniture in the house. The two benches that Pa hewed from logs before her father was born provided seating for the rest of the family.

George was sitting beside the stove whittling a horse for Eddie, the boy standing by his uncle's knee, patiently waiting. Mary was playing with a cow he'd made earlier in the day. In the summertime, George dug the red clay from the creek bed and used it to make toys for them.

Maggie had been sitting at the other side of the stove, holding Brenda Sue in her arms. Liphee was drying the last of the supper dishes when her mother asked if the baby was asleep. Liphee looked at her niece and saw that her face was red, her eyes open.

"Mommy, you better give her to me...how long has she been this quiet?"

Maggie handed Brenda into Liphee's outstretched arms.

"I haven't heard her cry to be fed since yesterday."

When Ginny entered the kitchen Liphee had the baby on the kitchen table and was removing her clothes to examine her for a rash. With no marks on her body and a dry diaper, Liphee asked when she'd last fed the baby and Ginny realized that the baby hadn't really nursed since early that morning.

"Liphee I tried to feed her earlier this mornin' when my milk came down but she wouldn't nurse, and she hasn't wanted to nurse since."

Maggie told Liphee and Ginny how to make a sugar teat to hold in Brenda's mouth. So all afternoon they took turns dropping the sweet liquid into the tiny mouth and Brenda swallowed. Ginny and Liphee took turns holding her through the long winter night and while they sat and rocked, the wind banked snow around the outer walls of three sides of the house.

Tuesday morning at daylight, Liphee walked to the nearest phone to place a call to the men in Ohio. The same storm that was paralyzing Eastern Kentucky was raging through three surrounding states. Liphee placed the call, left a message for her father and returned home to wait. When the men got the message to return home, they were stranded.

By the time the family realized that the men weren't coming, they were stranded in the holler. Wednesday morning, Liphee waded through the snow to the nearest neighbor who had a vehicle. She explained the situation and was promised a ride to the hospital. She again returned home to wait for help. The neighbor knocked at the door an hour later to tell them that his truck was stuck in a snowdrift. He promised to return for the baby when the roads were opened.

Liphee and Ginny held Brenda through another long night. They changed her diapers and tried to get her to swallow liquids. The baby dosed through the night held in her mother's arms. It was Friday afternoon before the road was plowed in front of the holler. By the time the neighbor got to the house, Charley and Ben had made it home. Ben and Ginny, with the baby followed the snowplow back to town, both praying that it wasn't too late to save Brenda Sue.

It was almost dark when Mary trudged through the path George had shoveled to the outhouse. She saw the truck lights coming up the holler. She finished her business and returned to the house as Ginny and Ben were getting out of the truck. Mary ran into the house to inform the rest of the family that they were back without the baby and Maggie told her that the doctor must have kept the baby in the hospital.

Instinctively, Charley knew, even before he saw their faces, that Brenda was not at the hospital. She had fallen

Across the Footbridge

asleep in the waiting room of the hospital. She died with her tiny fingers wrapped around one of her daddy's.

Three days later Charley and Maggie sat, silent, side by side, riding in the back of a neighbor's car. Tears ran down their cheeks to fall on the pine box that they held on their laps, the box where their granddaughter slept. The baby, who'd brought hope to a family on the brink of despair, was placed on the side of a little hill overlooking a small church. Her family returned to the holler following the funeral, somber and defeated.

Mary and Eddie sat by the stove in the front room, talking in whispers as if the baby was still asleep in the room, their conversation between the two children the only noise in the silent house. Occasionally, a lump of coal in the stove exploded from the heat surrounding it. The hiss of the water it held inside would sizzle when it touched the flames then fade into the silence. Ginny was lying on one bed in the bedroom and Maggie on the other.

Liphee was in the kitchen making supper for Mary and Eddie, her gaze continually returning to the small bouquet of plastic flowers Ginny carried home from the cemetery. Someone had laid the flowers on top of the old icebox. With the pain of the last two years churning inside her, she felt hatred rising from the depths of her soul. She was fifteen years old and had viewed poverty from close range for many of those years. She'd waded through snow with ice creeping into her shoes that had holes in their bottoms. She'd fed the last food in the house to the younger kids while her own stomach remained empty. She had watched her oldest sister withdraw into another world, go behind a wall that even

43

Pappy couldn't penetrate. But what she had witnessed the last week was harder for her to bear than all of her other years combined. She had stood helpless as the poverty she had always accepted as a part of her life robbed her family of the brightest thing they had ever known. Liphee stood in the kitchen the night of her niece's burial and acknowledged the death of her own girlhood as something inside her withered and died, leaving in its place the dull pain of hatred.

The days following the funeral slowly faded into weeks. Ginny returned to the inner world where she had spent most of the last two years. Maggie struggled to find strength to rise from her bed each day. Ben and Pappy never returned to Ohio. George took over the care of his young sister and nephew. Liphee silently cooked the meals and scrubbed the clothes on the washboard and draped them over chair backs to dry. The house filled with people became a quiet tomb, everyone continuously reminded of a tiny baby who had fleetingly touched all of their lives.

The last paycheck arrived from Ohio. With it spent, the men left the house each day searching for work. Some days all three worked and some days no one worked. But each day that money was earned they returned home with brightness in their eyes and the odor of wine on their breaths. Liphee resented the alcohol that bought them numbness to a pain she still had to carry.

When spring arrived in the holler word came that another mineshaft was going to be opened. Ginny had started to return for small spaces of time, each day coming a little closer to the family surrounding her, before again retreating into the inner world where no one could reach her. George,

Across the Footbridge

Pappy, and Ben returned to work with the opening of the new shaft. Their first weeks of labor spent digging and shoveling the red clay with the hope that a vein of coal lay on the other side.

By the time the summer's heat settled into the holler, Ginny had recovered enough to help with some of the work around the house. Because of her improvement Ben decided that it was time to establish a home again. He located two houses for rent on the same property and Charley and Maggie decided that a change would be good for all of them. The young couple would have privacy, yet the family would be close by in case Ginny relapsed. Everyone agreed the house they were leaving was a vault of bad memories.

In June of the year 1949, Ben and Ginny moved into their own home again. Each day that the mines were open he brought her and Eddie to her father's house at daybreak where he picked up Pappy and George. The three men rode to work together and returned in the afternoons and Ginny rode back home with Ben. By the end of the summer she was staying home some days with Eddie. Before the first frost of winter she knew that another baby would be born in early spring.

With the news of another pregnancy, the family again felt a heavy cloud settle over their lives. Through that winter Ginny remained strong, the baby inside her growing with the passing months. With her due date two weeks away, she and Ben returned to her parent's home. In the early morning of the first day of spring 1950, Ginny woke Ben and Liphee with a loud moan. Fifteen minutes later, Ben and Charley were rushing in the direction of Elly's house. They returned with her as Liphee was cutting the cord that attached her nephew to his mother. Larry Michael Rice had not waited for the mid-wife's help. Maggie had instructed Liphee in the tying and cutting of the umbilical cord.

Liphee stood at the side of her sister's bed looking into the face of another baby with red hair. In place of the delicate beauty she had viewed in Brenda Sue, she saw a determination in this infant's eyes. She held his small wet head to her breast and whispered a promise that only he and God heard.

"You, I will not lose."

Chapter Five

Ginny had no recognition of the son her body produced that morning. Liphee washed and dressed the baby, the mid-wife tending to the afterbirth. With Ginny's milk starting to flow, Liphee held Larry to his mother's breast.

After Larry's birth, Maggie retreated to her bed. It would take years to restore the inner strength she lost when she thought Ginny was going to die bringing another baby into the world. The men returned to the mines and Mary to school. Liphee spent her days washing diapers, watching over

Eddie, tending to her sister's body after childbirth and caring for an infant. She held the baby in the middle of the nights when everyone else was asleep. She sat in Pa's old rocker and whispered promises into his tiny ears. She felt that he didn't have a mother or father.

After his birth, Ginny retreated back to her other world and Ben returned to the house that they had shared. He still took George and Pappy to the mines each day and returned with them in the afternoons. Most days he went to the bed where Ginny lay where he stood looking down at her as he searched for a way to reach her.

Liphee watched the destructive force her family was crumbling under. Pappy's shoulders drooped from the fatigue of carrying pain for so long and Maggie quietly withdrew into her bed, lacking the will to rise and face the days. The strain in the house was evident on the faces of Eddie and Mary. Liphee continued moving through the days, but she felt as old as Pa's rocker. When she thought she could not face one more day, one more time, she looked at a baby, helpless and orphaned, and he would give her strength.

Larry was six weeks old when Ben stopped coming inside when he brought Pappy and George home. The following Saturday he came to visit with Eddie and give his father-in-law money for his family's upkeep. He'd closed the house he and Ginny shared; he was moving in with his brother. The next month he moved another woman into his bed.

The anger and pain Liphee felt the day she learned that Ben had moved on with his life was like a hot knife blade piercing her heart. She was suffering Ginny's pain and humiliation. Each week when he returned with money she

Across the Footbridge

again felt the heat of the anger wash over her. The week his girlfriend came to the holler with him, the anger exploded.

For years she'd swallowed back the pain as her family was repeatedly slammed with what felt like hell's own fury. When she saw another woman sitting beside her sister's husband, she saw her own fury. With one motion, she was at Ben's truck, her fist clutching a hand full of hair. When she refused to release what she held in her hand, Ben started the engine of the truck and put it in gear. Seconds later, Liphee was sitting fifty feet from where the truck had been parked with her toes bloody and her right hand still holding a fistful of hair. She looked at her feet then at the red hair in her hand and her tears started to fall. She sat in the middle of the road crying for a baby that had died and for one that had lived. She cried for the mother who was removed from them both.

For six months, each day in the house was repetitive of the one before. The growth of an infant into a smiling baby was the only indication that time was moving them forward. Larry was six months and three weeks old, when Ginny spoke to Liphee. She had started her journey back. Within two months, she was caring for her own sons.

Liphee turned eighteen in September. That winter, Ben started staying a little longer each week when he came to bring money. Soon he was talking of returning to his family. He'd taken a job hauling coal over the road. In the spring, Ginny went on a couple of runs with him but the reconciliation that the family had come to expect never materialized. In June he moved in with his girlfriend. In July, Liphee learned that Ginny was pregnant.

With Larry in her arms, she acknowledged the fact that

49

another baby would arrive that winter. She prayed through the fall for the strength to accept what she could not leave.

Ginny was alert throughout the pregnancy and she and Liphee shared some of the camaraderie of their youths. If either had thoughts of what lay waiting for them in the future, it wasn't discussed. With Ginny's health restored, Pappy and George began to regain some of the energy that the last two years had drained from them. Mary and Eddie were once again chasing each other around the house and up the hills. Mary was eleven; Eddie turned seven that October. Maggie was still confined to her bed but with Ginny helping with the chores, Liphee's burden was lighter than it'd been in years. She started to have youthful dreams when Ginny teased her about the prince that would find his way up the holler looking for her. Ben still came by occasionally if he had a few dollars to contribute. The more noticeable Ginny's pregnancy became, the more space he put between his visits.

By the first week of December, Ginny's toes had again disappeared from her view. By the second week, she struggled to rise from the bed and the seat in the outhouse. On December 16, 1952, the sun barely penetrated the cold wind that blew between the hills to find its way under the doors and through the cracks around the windows of the house. George and Pappy carried in extra coal for two stoves they would keep fires in that night. By bedtime, Ginny had a backache. Liphee stayed up with her after the rest of the family went to bed, the two sisters talking till late in the night before finally drifting towards sleep.

Liphee was awakened two hours later. Ginny was in labor and the baby's head was visible with each contraction.

Across the Footbridge

Pappy and George left the holler at five a.m. on December 17, to bring the mid-wife. When they arrived at her house they found Elly in the barn milking cows. By the time she put her milk away and returned to the truck with her bag, it was five-forty. Roger Rice was born at five-forty-three a.m. December 17, 1952.

When the mid-wife walked into the bedroom, Liphee was holding an infant. Blood was starting to seep off the sheets Liphee had placed under Ginny and drip onto the floor. She'd been hemorrhaging for more than fifteen minutes. Liphee placed the baby on the bed she had been sleeping in an hour before and went to the kitchen for water to wash another new life. She hung a quilt over the doorway of the room where the mid-wife worked to stop her sister's bleeding. Liphee worked for the next hour, washing her nephew and placing him in bed with his grandmother, then washing the floor of her sister's blood.

It was two hours before the mid-wife felt reasonably sure that Ginny would live. In those hours Pappy and Maggie died a dozen times. Liphee died once. When she saw her sister's paralyzed face, she silently cursed the power that had set out to destroy them. Ginny had almost bled to death giving birth to a baby that she might leave before she was aware of his existence.

Ginny didn't die and this time she didn't withdraw from her family. Maybe, God knew the family could not withstand anymore. Perhaps, he was looking in another direction three weeks later. The old iron stove that'd warmed them for more than three generations almost took all of their lives the first week of January. Everyone was out of the house when the roof fell into the flames. Pappy stood watching, burns covering most of his face and both of his arms, as the flames made cinders of everything he owned except his wife, children, and grandchildren.

Across the Footbridge

Chapter Six

The warm air that the big truck breathed out of its exhaust pipe mixed with the cold air of the January dusk to create a thick haze of fog and smoke that erased the house behind. Ben opened the door of the truck and leaned half way out to see how close he was to the house. When he was within a few feet of the front porch, he shut off the engine and slowly climbed down from the cab of the truck. He'd left home at three o'clock that morning. Jessie wanted him home at night even if it meant him leaving in the middle of the night before. He would never understand her logic. Sometimes, he wondered what he saw in her; other times he wondered what she saw in him.

How was it possible for one man to mess up his life so bad in less than forty years? The question he'd asked himself over and over for the last year or so never answered itself. Maybe if there was an answer, he didn't want to hear it. A man of his years with five sons should know all of the answers.

He used to tell himself that the reason he didn't go see his two boys by his first marriage was because of Ginny. After they were married, she needed time to adjust. Then she was pregnant, and he thought that he'd take her and the baby to meet his other children at the same time. Then she got sick and the baby came and died. He never found the right time or the needed courage to go see his sons or to take Ginny with him. Now she wasn't in his life and he still couldn't go. How could he face his mother and father and tell them that he had three more sons that he didn't live with? How could he take Jessie to his parents' home when they thought he was living with Ginny?

Ben set his dinner bucket down on the end of the porch and headed in the direction of the outhouse. He needed a little more time before he went inside to face Jessie. She was everything that Ginny wasn't. With red hair, heavy breasts, and wide hips, she never reminded him of his wife. That was the first thing that attracted his attention. Jessie was so different from Ginny. He still remembered the first time he saw Ginny; she couldn't have been more than seventeen or so.

Ben had an appointment with an attorney that day. The lawyer's office was in the big bank building uptown and he parked his truck across the street from it. He wanted to

Across the Footbridge

find out if he could legally place his two sons with other family members. He couldn't take care of two little boys himself and he sure didn't want their mother to have them. Any woman that'd sleep with a man she wasn't married too wasn't a proper mother in his eyes. He was going to give his oldest son to his mother and dad. The two-year-old had already been placed with one of his sisters. He needed to find out if his soon to be ex-wife could legally get the kids back.

Ben had just closed his truck door when he saw the girl and an older man walking out of the door he was heading for. He watched them leave the building and cross the street to the bus stop. When they took a seat he knew that they were waiting for the bus that ran out into the county each afternoon. He thought about canceling his appointment and offering them a ride. He knew he'd waited three weeks for the appointment; three more weeks could possibly turn his kids back over to their mother. He continued on into the building. There were doctor and lawyer's offices on the top floors. He wondered if the man and girl had been to see a doctor or an attorney as he was. When he left the building an hour later the bench across the street was empty.

Almost three years passed before he saw her again. He still remembered her. She reminded him of an Indian girl in a story he'd read when he was in school. He was surprised that he remembered the story after all those years but he wasn't surprised that he remembered the girl. She had the same long black hair and her body was still caught somewhere between a girl and a full-grown woman. This time he recognized what had caught his attention the first time. She had the body of a very desirable woman, yet she seemed totally unaware of her beauty. She had walked close to the man who turned out to be her father as if she was still a small girl. She's shy, he thought the second time he saw her.

She was with a young man and younger girl who turned out to be her sister and brother. When he got close enough to see her face he realized that her eyes were black. He'd never seen black eyes before. Her high cheekbones reminded him again of an Indian girl. This time he found out who she was and where she lived. They were talking to a man he'd worked with a few years before.

He drove past the holler for two weeks before he finally saw her father walking home from work. He slowed down, and offered him a ride. Fortunately, the man was carrying two sacks of groceries. Ginny's father was happy not to have to carry the heavy bags the last mile. Ben parked his truck in front of the house where Charley directed him and he carried one of the bags inside. Within two weeks, he was driving Charley and George to work and back. The next week he started picking Ginny and George up on Sunday evenings to take them to church. He always returned when the services were over to drive them back home. Six months later he and Ginny stood in front of her father as man and wife.

How did his plans get destroyed so fast? He had cheated on his first wife before he caught her in bed with someone else. He'd promised his mother that he would never cheat on Ginny. His mother talked to him after he told both of his parents he was going to be married again. His dad spoke his piece about not bringing any more kids home for them to raise then he walked out of the room. Ben's mother took her son's hand in one of her own, as he was ready to leave the

Across the Footbridge

table. She looked at him over the leftovers of their Sunday meal.

"I know your dad didn't mean we won't love anymore kids you bring into the world. Ben, were both old now, we can't live forever. Make sure your marriage is sound before you git Ginny pregnant. She's young and she's a good girl. I knew her grandmother when we were both girls. Ben, if you love her, you marry her an' if you marry her, you be true to her."

Ben Rice promised his mother the Sunday before he and Ginny were married that Ginny would be the only woman he would ever lay down with again.

He thought of that promise when he picked his dinner buckct up from the porch and walked through the door of Jessie's house. Seven years latcr he was sleeping in someone else's bed. Hc closed the door against the night air and hollered into the doorway that led to the kitchen.

"Jessie, I'm back!"

She was quiet that night and he felt the old familiar fear starting to take control of his thoughts. Surely, she wasn't slippin' around with someone else while he was driving all day and half the night. The Saturday night she'd been so adamant about having turned out to be a quiet evening. After they ate, Jessie complained of a headache and retrcated to the bed they shared. Ben was relieved. He was tired, and tonight he didn't feel up to a session of Jessie. His last thoughts before falling asleep were of his wife.

Jessie knew the next morning that she should tell him before someone else did. If he was going to leave, she wanted to know it now. She needed to find out if he loved her or not

57

and she'd know by his reaction to her news.

She placed his coffee cup and spoon in front of his breakfast plate. She poured scalding coffee in the cup, set the pot on the stove, and moved back across the kitchen to stand behind his chair.

"Ben... something happened while you were gone yesterday."

He felt the heat rising from his neck. He just wanted to know who she'd been with, and then he would leave. He should've known he'd never be able to trust a woman with red hair.

Jessie took a deep breath and finished telling him what he'd have to know.

"Right before daybreak yesterday, the house that Charley and Mag were living in burned to the ground. I went by there about seven yesterday morning and the smoke was still raising from the remains. Nobody was around. I asked around yesterday and nobody would tell me if they got out... or where the kids are if they did."

Slowly he raised from his chair and turned around to face her.

"Jessie, you went by there to see if I was there, didn't you?" Her words were lost in the noise of the glass and coffee crashing into the wall behind the stove.

"I didn't mean it Ben. You know I trust you!"

It took him two hours to find someone who knew what had happened the day before. During those hours, he faced the possibility that his wife and three of his sons could be dead. He accepted his responsibility for what he prayed hadn't happened. For the first time since he'd pulled his dead daughter's fingers from one of his, he talked to the power above, the one his mother was convinced was there.

He poured out his soul over the rumbling noise of the truck's engine. He knew that if there was a God he already knew what he was confessing, but he wanted him to know that he was ready to admit it out loud.

He told of the pain that he had suffered being his father's son because he knew about the other women his dad had met in town. As a kid he'd sat in front of the old motel on the outskirts of the county seat waiting for his dad to come out of the room he'd entered hours before. Later, he had remained silent when his father told his mother about the long lines that they waited in to pay the taxes.

He told his silent companion of the humiliation he'd suffered being the only son his father produced to disgrace the family name with a divorce and he'd never been the provider that his brothers had been.

He told of the fear and the jealousy that he suffered when Ginny went to that other world, the one that separated them. After the shock of seeing her totally lost in her own mind, he'd suffered again when he and Pappy took her to that doctor in town. He realized that day that the appointment they'd had in the bank building all those years ago had been to see the same doctor. The doctor told him and Pappy that there wasn't much they could do. They could commit her to a sanitarium, but he advised against it. He said she should come out of it eventually. The people, who went to the institution at the southern part of the state, usually didn't get better.

The doctor had been right. Ginny had gotten better. Then Brenda Sue died and she got sick again. He thought she was gone for good that time. He could still remember the anger he felt when she left after Larry was born. His birth had reminded Ben of Brenda Sue. When Ginny didn't come around after his birth, he blamed the baby. He still remembered the times he went to Ginny's bed, trying to talk to her with his heart. He had stood at the side of the bed where she lay, pleading with her to take him with her wherever it was that she went. He asked to be forgiven for the anger he felt when she refused to talk to him, refused to take him with her. It had been that anger that drove him to Jessie. Ben confessed it all in the cab of the truck as he drove from house to house, asking people he knew if they knew where his family was. By the time he was out of words and out of sins, he was ready to offer a bargain. He asked any God that might be listening to give him just one more chance. He promised on his baby's grave that he'd never leave Ginny again, just let her and the boys be alive.

The man, who owned the store about five miles from Jessie's house, knew where his family was staying. They'd gone to a relative's of Charley's after the fire. The old woman had offered to let the entire family stay in her basement in return for Liphee cleaning the house and doing her laundry. The storekeeper relayed all the events of the day before to Ben. He said Ginny's dad had been burned pretty bad trying to see to it that all of the kids got out safe.

Ben thanked the merchant and returned to his truck. Before starting the engine, he spoke his thanks into the silent air. He left the store, headed in the direction of his folks' farm. He intended to ask his dad to take him in while he looked for a place to take his wife and kids to.

Chapter Seven

The closest neighbor saw the light from the fire in the skyline when he went to the barn to check on a new calf. He thought about the two houses that were in the vicinity of the fire, knowing that one was vacant. He hoped that it was the one on fire. A lot of people lived in the other house. He'd spoken to his wife about the situation. He thought at least five adults and maybe three or four kids were crowded into that three-room house. At first they'd rented both of the houses in the holler but after a while the one man left and the woman with the two little kids moved in with the others. That was back before Christmas. He saw her in the yard one day when he was up that way hunting. She had a baby in her arms. The little guy couldn't have been more'n a year and a half old and her belly was already big with another child. He'd seen her husband in town earlier that day with a redheaded woman. He remembered coming home and telling his wife about it.

Now, looking in the direction of the two little houses, if he was a praying man, he'd have asked the Lord to let the house on fire be the empty one. After checking his calf and its mother, he went inside the house and woke his wife to tell her he'd better go check out the fire in the next holler. Ten minutes later, the beams of his car lights silhouetted the family huddled together as they watched the roof of their home fall to the ground.

The neighbor offered to take the kids home to his wife. Charley thanked him, then told him that as frightened as the kids were they'd better stay with the family. He asked for a ride to a relative's house.

By noon, the family was settled into the bottom of Aunt Arissa's house. She relented and took them in because her sons could use a break with the upkeep of the big house. It'd been years since she'd felt up to doing her work herself and the two grown boys that her husband saddled her with when he died didn't always clean as good as she wished. She never understood the powers that gave her nephew, Charley, three daughters to go along with his sons and never even gave her one girl. She could put up with the rest of the family until Liphee got her house whipped into shape again, but she told them that they'd have to keep the kids in the basement, and keep them quiet. After all, her heart wasn't as strong as it used to be.

By suppertime, Charley and Mag were deeply indebted to the neighbor who'd introduced himself to them that morning. He hauled the whole family to Aunt Arissa's, then returned about three hours later with the back seat of his car filled with clothes, blankets, and dishes. He apologized for not having more to bring.

Beds were made for the little kids out of cardboard boxes placed on chairs that Arissa stored in the basement. She had her sons bring one bed down from the attic for the family to use. That night Liphee made a spot for everyone to sleep, then fell exhausted onto the pile of quilts that was her and Ginny's bed. The next morning she had to scrub the ceiling and walls in her aunt's kitchen.

Charley lay awake until he was sure that everyone else was asleep before he turned to his wife lying beside him, staring, through unseeing eyes.

"Mag, I don't know how we're gonna do it, but I'll not allow this to destroy our family."

She turned her head in his direction as if she could still see the face that was branded into her memory and her heart.

"Charley, the only regret I have is the pain our lives has brought on you and the younguns'. I'd rather be homeless with you, than be anywhere else without you."

"Mag, I promised the Good Lord I wouldn't complain again if he didn't take Ginny from us after Roger was born. I just wish my hands hadn't been burnt so bad in the fire cause I don't know how long it'll be before I'll be able to work again."

Maggie raised her right hand and placed it on the covers separating it from her husband's heart.

Across the Footbridge

"Charley, it may take awhile, but we'll be okay."

By the time that they'd been in the basement two weeks, Liphee knew something would have to change. She'd spent every day except Sunday upstairs, scrubbing, cooking and running errands for her aunt. The second week, she started going to the barn twice a day to milk the cows. Arissa told her she could have part of the milk and butter the cows produced for the kids. The only other food she gave them was a bushel of potatoes she had her son bring up from the root cellar. Liphee cooked the potatoes for her family on the old stove in the basement that her aunt used to do her canning. The little kids could smell the aroma of the food cooking upstairs but all they got to eat was what was left over.

At the end of the second week, Liphee told her father that she was going to town the next day to find a job and a place for them to live; George was caring for the family downstairs anyway, while she spent most of her waking hours working for her aunt. If she worked herself into an early grave, it wouldn't be to keep her family in an underground prison.

The following day she hitched a ride into town and by nightfall she'd found a job caring for a handicapped man and his elderly mother. She stayed there through the week. On Friday, she spent part of her first week's wages on food for the family and bus fare to take it to them. When Liphee walked into the damp basement that Friday night, she took more than food with her, she took hope and determination. She returned to town on Sunday. The next Friday she found an apartment to rent.

Aunt Arissa and her sons were sad that the family was leaving so soon. The boys needed time to do the repair work in the barn they'd been putting off for several years. They'd both enjoyed doing man's work again, returning to the house at mealtimes to enjoy what someone else had cooked. Arissa'd been disappointed that Liphee wouldn't be there to do the spring cleaning that she been planning to do once the weather got warmer.

The neighbor that brought them clothes after the fire was kind enough to move the family and their few possessions into town. The apartment was meagerly furnished but they'd be able to replace their beds and other furniture someday. The first three weeks were rough. The man Liphee worked for advanced her enough money to pay the rent on the apartment, withholding part of what she earned each week until the loan was paid. There was barely money left to buy enough food to keep the family from starving.

They'd been in the apartment three weeks when someone knocked at the door on a Sunday afternoon. Liphee, who had Sunday's off from her job, opened the door expecting to find the man who lived in the apartment downstairs. He occasionally came to the door to complain of the noise that the kids made running through the hallway. Each time he came, he had a treat or toy tucked under his arm.

Liphee opened the door with a smile on her face, wondering what he'd thought to bring the kids. The smile disappeared when she saw him. Five weeks after he moved in with his folks, Ben summonsed up the courage to face his wife's family.

When Liphee looked at Ben all the events of the past weeks rushed through her mind. Pappy had walked the floor four days and nights with the pain from his burns. She remembered the day Aunt Arissa caught her with the chunk of butter she'd been sneaking downstairs to give to her daddy to rub on his face and arms. That was the day Liphee added the barn chores to her already overburdened days. The conversation was still imbedded in her mind.

"Liphee, is that grease on that dress I gave you? If I 'd known you weren't gonna take care of it better'n that, I'd have saved it to give to somebody else."

Liphee recalled the hatred that came rushing up from the depths of her tired soul.

"Aunt Arissa, you didn't give me the dress! Remember? I traded you for it with one the neighbor brought us. That one didn't fit any of us an' I traded it for this one. This one you were gonna have me tear into rags to clean the floors with."

"Liphee where're you going with that butter? If you wanted butter... you should've asked me. Tomorrow when you milk the cows, you save some of the cream you skim off the top and take it down to the kids. When you fill the new butter tub, then you can take the old butter downstairs instead of throwing it to the hogs."

Charley almost went behind Arissa's house three days after the fire to place one of his hands on the chopping block and bring the ax down on it with the other. He knew he wouldn't be able to cut the other one off with a bloody stub and the family didn't need the pain of him bleeding to death in the back yard. On the fifth day new skin started to form and five weeks later he could bear the weight of a cup of coffee in his hands for the first time. He'd hated the weeks George and Liphee spoon-fed him like they did the little kids. Just that

Across the Footbridge

morning, he felt good enough to tease Mag about all the money that he was saving on haircuts. The blaze from the fire had singed the front of his hair and face. He was beginning to wonder if he'd ever have to shave again. He figured that in three more weeks he'd have enough new skin on his hands to go back to work. He still thought of the butter that Liphee had rubbed on his hands each time she changed his dressings. That butter kept the strips of old sheets from pulling the new skin off each time the bandages were removed. He'd said to Mag just that morning, "That Liphee, she's our blessing."

Ginny was finally using the side of her body the stroke had paralyzed. Her face still told the tale of Roger's birth, but her speech improved every day. Once Liphee managed to get them out of the basement, the whole family started to heal. Mary and Eddie started at the school in town the week they moved. It was good for both of the kids to be away from the pain and suffering for a while each day.

Larry had started watching Eddie use the bathroom down the hall the week before and for the last two days Roger was the only little guy to be diapered. For the first time in his life, George took a real interest in one of his nephew's personal habits. Liphee teased him about it when she came home Friday night. She told him that he should've been washing diapers years ago. All of the kids would have potty broken sooner.

Mag, still confined to her bed, was somewhere warm and dry. George teased the little kids as he used to tease his sisters. Roger spent the bigger part of his days lying by his grandmother, reaching for his ten fat toes.

These were the memories flooding through Liphee

when Ben spoke.

"Hi Liphee, how've you all been?"

It took a lot of strength to keep from slamming the door in his face, strength she gained from the sight of the bag Ben held towards her. Jutting out of the bag of groceries was a box of baby cereal just like the one that she'd promised Roger, because he was keeping his mommy busy trying to keep him fed.

The bag contained all the things that they were in need of, things that they hadn't seen since before the fire. When Ben left that afternoon, fifteen dollars was laying on the kitchen table.

On Monday, Charley received a letter from his oldest son. Gar had mailed his father three letters that'd been returned. He had married a girl from the next town that he'd met right after the war and they were living in Florida. His younger brother Willie was stationed in Maryland and was engaged to be married. For the first time in more years than he cared to count, Charley slept the sleep of a grateful parent that night.

Four weeks later, Pappy and George returned to the mines. Liphee still worked for the man in town. Ginny was strong enough to manage Larry and Roger during the days when the men were at work and the older kids were at school. The first week of June 1953, Charley moved them into a better apartment, bought beds for them to sleep in and an old car that he was making payments on. The family was slowly regaining their strength when Liphee met the man she would marry. By the first of September, Ben and Ginny were again living under the same roof.

Across the Footbridge

Eddie remembered his father but the other two boys' affections had to be earned. Ben was patient as he paid for the months he had neglected his family. At Christmas time, Liphee worked her last week for the man in town. She took eight dollars from her last week's wages and gave the rest to her father. She wore a new dress costing seven dollars and fifty cents when she went to the county courthouse that Friday. She walked out of the building twenty minutes later with a new last name.

The man she married didn't know poverty as she did. His parents owned the house they had brought up ten kids in. The first time Liphee went to their home for dinner she saw more food on their table for that one meal than her family had ever eaten in a month. The pans Paul's mother cooked with were almost as large as the ones she washed the kids and laundry in at home. She was shy, felt out of place. After her first trip there, she felt that she was not suited to be Paul's wife and she explained this to him when he returned her to the apartment. He apologized for not being able to bring her food all of the times she'd been hungry and promised her she would never know that pain again. He wanted to be at her side.

When Liphee married Paul, Ginny and the kids had been living with Ben for three months. He had rented another house up another holler to take his family to. The week after Liphee moved her few things into her new home, Charley and Maggie moved out of the apartment and into a house on the outskirts of town and it seemed strange to have only four people in a house. Mary was almost twelve years old. She came home from school each day to cook supper for her father, mother, and brother. The house seemed quiet to

Across the Footbridge

Charley and Mag after the years they'd shared their home with Ginny and their grandchildren. Ben brought Ginny and the kids in to visit each weekend. Every week that Ginny remained strong Charley gave thanks again for the bargain that he made with God the day that Roger was born. In January 1954, Ginny told her mother and father that she was pregnant. She also told them that she wanted a girl this time.

Paul rented a small apartment two blocks from the house he grew up in and he took Liphee there on their wedding night. It was the first time she slept on store bought fitted sheets. When she turned down their bed that night, she thought of the yards of muslin she'd sewn together at home for sheets. The next morning she woke up on sheets that were still tucked under at the corners. That week, Paul took her shopping for clothes and she felt worldly going into a department store to look for a dress that fit instead of making someone else's dress fit her. Each day she went to the kitchen of their little apartment and opened the cupboard doors to see the food that was always there. Each time she sat down to a meal with Paul she thought of the years with little or nothing her family had survived. Paul had a normal job with normal pay. Her family had never had the luxury of just being normal people. Each weekend she took one or two of the little boys to the apartment where Paul shared in her joy of treating them to the ice cream and candy she'd never been able to give them before. They both looked forward to the day they could treat a son or daughter of their own.

The news of Ginny's pregnancy put a damper on Liphee's happiness. She had shared her life and the events of her family with her husband, Paul, and he assured her that he'd

Across the Footbridge

be at her side if things went wrong again. He also reminded her that the entire family had suffered enough.

"This time things'll be different, you'll see."

That spring the baby that Ginny was carrying seemed to take over her whole body. At seven months, she struggled to reach the training pants that insisted on falling down around Roger's feet as she encouraged him in his efforts of making trips to the outhouse. It would be enough work washing diapers on a washboard for one baby. She reminded him that he wanted to be a big boy like his two older brothers. The third week of May, Ben brought Ginny and the boys to Pappy's where they would stay until the baby came. He returned to the house in the country but planned to come to visit them each weekend. After Ginny recovered from the baby's birth, he would take his family back home.

The mine, that Pappy and George returned to work at after the fire, closed the first week of March but they both found jobs the same week at the cemetery at the edge of town. Ben started hauling gravel after the vein of coal ran out, while all three men waited for another mineshaft to open. The two weeks the family waited for the baby's arrival were long and tense. Paul brought Liphee to Pappy's house every night after he got off work. The last week of May they told the three boys that they'd be coming to their house after the baby was born.

On the first day of June the pains started in Ginny's back. Her last three babies had been born within hours of her first cramps. This time it took three days and when she looked at the baby girl that Elly lay on her stomach the third day of June 1954, she knew that this time she'd hold the baby and nurse it herself. This time she'd be okay.

Liphee and Paul took three tired boys to their apartment the night their sister was born. Ben kissed Ginny before he left for the house in the country. That night, each member of her family breathed a sigh of relief. Ginny had been in labor for most of three days but the last hours had resulted in a baby girl Ginny held to her own breast for her first feeding.

The night his second granddaughter was born, Charley placed his hand over the one his wife placed over his heart.

"Mag, I think she's gonna to be okay this time."

"Charley, your ma always said that the Lord won't put no more on us than what we can bear."

"Mag, I hope that you 'n Ma are right this time."

Chapter Eight

The dust particles from the last load of gravel floated up to find a resting-place in the cab of the old truck, the sunlight filtering through them as Ben headed the truck in the direction of home. He'd just dumped the last load of gravel for the day. Excitement had been building in him for the last week. He guessed it felt similar to how those tiny particles of gravel dust would feel if they could have feelings and had a voice to express them. He was going home to clean up a little and then go get his wife and kids. The house'd sure been quiet in the evenings he'd spent there alone. Ginny and the kids had been staying at her daddy's for nine weeks. Every day that they'd been gone, he'd reminded himself that they'd be coming

73

home soon because every week he went to visit them and found Ginny alert and in her right mind. Each trip convinced him a little more that this time she'd really come home.

Charley was concerned about the distance that would soon separate Ginny from the rest of her family. She would be forty miles away without any family close-by. He and Mag talked about it again the night before. He thought about sending George home with her, but he wanted her to believe that she'd be okay. He knew if he sent her brother home with her, she'd sense his doubt.

"Mag, I don't know what to do. I wanna believe that this time she'll be okay."

The fear that had haunted him for more than ten years was again creeping into his heart. His last sentence hung in the air after he heard the regular breathing that told him his wife was asleep.

"Mag, I know you don't wanna believe it...but one day when I'm dead 'n gone, she'll get away from the rest of you, an' Ginny'll destroy herself."

He lay awake a long time thinking about what could happen when Ginny and the boys went home the next day.

It was July 24, 1954. Eddie and Larry released the minnows they'd been collecting for the last three days from the hole they'd dug at the edge of the creek bed. Each day the two boys went to the creek right after breakfast. They watched the minnows eat the biscuit crumbs that they dropped in the water while Larry anticipated having a real fish farm someday. Today, the wall of clay and sticks that separated the minnows from the rest of the creek had been torn down. Eddie told Larry that the baby fish would die when they weren't around

Across the Footbridge

to keep the hole filled with water. Larry watched the minnows find their way through the crack in the wall that Eddie made. Within seconds, the minnows disappeared into the creek. The two boys stood on the creek bank watching the walls of their fish tank disintegrate little by little, as the stream captured the wall that the boys had spent most of the Monday before constructing.

The clothes and diapers that Ginny and the kids had used for the last nine weeks were packed and ready on the front porch for Ben should be there soon. Ginny was eager to get home. She stood on the front porch of her parents' home looking towards the driveway on the other side of the creek. She saw her father and brother when they entered the drive and headed for the path that'd lead them to the footbridge. Before they reached the bridge, she heard the familiar sound of Ben's big truck. By the time Pappy and George reached the porch, Eddie and Larry were running up from under the bridge. Ginny smiled at the sight of her sons racing across the bridge and over the path to their father. An hour later, Ben, Ginny, and the four kids were squeezed into the cab of the old truck as it made its way towards the county highway. They were going home.

The heat from the day hung in the air that night. Charley lay awake listening to the sounds of the late night filtering through the open windows. He was still awake when the two a.m. train made its way down the tracks that ran parallel with the road. He thought of the silence that Ginny'd be listening to, if she too were awake. By now she was miles away from the nearest train track. The house where Ben took her and the kids was almost a mile from the nearest phone.

75

Across the Footbridge

The home Ginny took her daughter to was at the end of another holler and one house stood between them and the county road that was their access to civilization. The man living in the house always raised his hand in greeting when he saw Ben and his family pass. The fact that someone else lived in the holler, comforted Ben during the days that he left Ginny and the kids home alone. It looked as if Paul'd been right when he said there were better times ahead for them. Each day Ben returned home from work to find his wife as he'd left her that morning. Supper was always waiting for him with the day's laundry waving a welcome from the clothesline as he drove over ruts that were starting to resemble a driveway.

Peggy Ann was four months old when an early frost transformed the leftovers in the garden into a frosty winter scene. The house absorbed the cold of the night before as if it was readying itself to preserve a butchered hog. Ben started the first fire of the season in the stove in the front room before he left for work. When he returned that afternoon the only sign that remained of the unseasonable frost was the droop the sun had brought to the garden that day. When he entered the house, Ginny was sitting on the side of the bed rocking back and forth with a crying baby on her shoulder. There were no signs of supper in the kitchen. The cold of the night before left Peggy Ann with a temperature and congested lungs. Ben made supper for the boys and watched as Ginny paced the rooms of the house with a baby riding on her shoulder. By breakfast time, the temperature outside had plummeted to an all time low while inside Peggy struggled to breathe, her parents readying her for a trip to the hospital. In his rush to get the baby to the doctor, Ben put enough coal on the fire to

Across the Footbridge

keep the house warm for the hours he thought they might be gone. An hour later, his truck rumbled to a stop in front of Liphee and Paul's apartment. Halfway to town, Ginny realized that they had left three young boys sleeping in the house with a roaring fire in the stove that stood between them and the front door. Ben left the engine running while he knocked at Liphee's door. He asked her and Paul to go get the boys and bring them back to their house.

Liphee was quiet on the drive to the country, her mind replaying the scene of the fire that'd almost taken her life and the lives of her family three years before. She had the car door open before Paul brought the car to a complete stop and opened the door to the warm air in the kitchen and the sight of three boys seated around a breakfast table. The neighbor at the end of the holler had seen Ben's truck race past his house early that morning and when he saw Ben and Ginny in the truck, he went up the holler to make sure the missing faces were okay. Liphee thanked the man and the force that protected her nephews. Paul poured cold ashes that he found in a bucket by the kitchen door on the fire in the stove before they loaded up the three boys and headed towards town.

When Paul and Liphee reached the hospital they found Ben and Ginny sitting in the hallway in front of the room where Peggy Ann had been for the last two hours. Ginny, seeing her sister coming towards her, rose from her seat. Paul could see the fear in Ginny's eyes and Liphee saw the beginnings of something else.

Fifteen minutes later, a tired doctor walked through the door that separated them from the baby. He told them it'd been a close one and Peggy Ann would need to stay in the hospital for a while, but she would be okay.

They watched the baby through the oxygen tent that assisted her small lungs in their effort to provide her body with life. Liphee watched Ginny begin to struggle with the force that was returning to lay claim to their lives.

Ben and Paul took Ginny with them when they left the hospital an hour later. Liphee stayed with Peggy Ann and Ginny returned to Pappy's where Liphee and Paul had left the boys that morning. Pappy and Mag were waiting for news, the family united in their fear of losing another baby.

Peggy Ann stayed in the hospital for eight days. When she was released, she went home with Ginny to Pappy's. Liphee and Paul took the boys to their apartment and Ben returned to the house in the country. Ginny was fighting the force that was attempting to remove her from her family one more time and again a new routine was established.

During the week, while the rest of the family was at work or school, Ginny and Mag were alone with Peggy Ann with Mag talking to Ginny through the mornings that they waited for Liphee to arrive with the two younger boys. After Paul and Eddie ate their breakfast and left the apartment for the day, Liphee dressed Larry and Roger and took them to Pappy's to spend the rest of the day. Ginny seemed capable of managing the baby for a few hours. Ben returned each weekend to visit with his family as they waited to see if Ginny would triumph over the disease that was trying to remove her again.

Two weeks after the baby was released from the hospital, the doctor told Liphee that Peggy was free from the effects of the pneumonia. The next morning when she returned to her parents' house for her daily visit she opened the door and heard her mother calling Ginny's name.

"Liphee, is that you? I've been trying to get Ginny to answer me for the last two hours. The baby's been crying to be fed, and she won't answer when I call her name."

Larry and Roger were standing behind her when Liphee saw the blood coming from the baby's mouth.

"You boys go to your grandmother's bed, Now!"

Ginny was sitting in a chair in the front room. At her feet was the blanket where Peggy Ann lay, her fist clutching a piece of broken glass that she was trying to suck nourishment from. Liphee picked her up and washed the dried blood off her face. When she was assured that the cuts were minor and the baby had no glass in her mouth, she held her to her mother's breast. Ginny continued to stare at the invisible object in front of her unaware that her sister was unbuttoning her blouse. As soon as Pappy and George returned from the cemetery, Liphee went to purchase bottles, Carnation milk, and corn syrup. It was three days later when Peggy Ann accepted the bottle her aunt offered her, for the first time without protest. With her weaned from her mother's milk, Liphee took the baby with her when she went home that night.

Peggy Ann was almost three years old when she returned to live with her parent's and many events took place in the years that she lived with Liphee. Her father closed the door on another house in the country and moved in with his wife's family and when the family that rented the house in front of Charley and Mag moved a few weeks later, Liphee and Paul moved there the following week. By the time Peggy Ann took her first wobbly steps, her grandfather was within hollering distance and Liphee carried her across the bridge to share their accomplishment with the rest of the family.

The three boys now had the area of two yards to explore and the haven of two houses to run to. And, as he promised, this time Ben remained at his wife's side as she struggled to find her way back to the family. Liphee and Paul left their kitchen door unlocked when they turned out their lights for the night when they tucked Eddie and Peggy Ann in for the night before going to lie in their bed and discuss the child of their own that failed to become a reality. Peggy Ann was two years old when Ginny started her long journey back. That summer, Pappy and Mag moved from the house they were living in to the one next door and Ben moved in there the same day that Pappy moved out.

Liphee watched through her kitchen window each afternoon for the three men to pass. Pappy, Ben and George were all gravediggers. Larry and Roger lived with Ginny and Ben and Peggy Ann spent part of each day with her mother. When bedtime came, she whined for the bed in the corner of her aunt and uncle's bedroom. Eddie had remained with Liphee and Paul when his younger brothers returned home. By the time Ginny returned to the family, Pappy was ready to leave.

Liphee had noticed his steps getting slower when he passed her window each afternoon, and he seemed to shrink in the months that followed. Finally, she confronted him as always before he had confronted her about her health. She had miscarried twice in the years that she and Paul had been trying to have their own child.

"Pappy, you're gonna have to go to a doctor. Mary told me that you've been throwing up blood in the mornings

Across the Footbridge

before you leave for work."

"Liphee, I don't need to pay a doctor to tell me that I've got an ulcer. I'm surprised I've even got a stomach left after the last two years."

He was holding Peggy on his lap. Earlier that day, he found a little basket in the dump at the cemetery. The glass basket had flowers molded into its side and he cleaned the dirt off and brought it to Peggy Ann. The basket reminded him of the granddaughter who died years before. Peggy sat on his knee examining the treasure.

Three weeks later, a surgeon left Charley on an operating table to go to the room where the family waited. He told them that the cancer was so widespread he could do nothing more than close the incision and send him home to die.

Mary was fourteen years old when she returned to the house she'd now share with her mother and brother. That day, she watched her father be lowered into a hole beside a grave that he helped dig two months before. He was buried in the cemetery at the edge of town. Paul bought the plot where he was buried and the one adjoining it. The stone he had placed on the graves two months later, had Maggie Sexton's name and date of birth engraved on it along with her husband's name, date of birth, and date of death. Two months later, Peggy Ann returned to her parents' house to spend the night for the first time in more than two years. It was Memorial Day, 1957, one week before her third birthday.

Chapter Nine

Ginny returned after more than two years to discover that her father had died in her absence. The void his death left in her heart was hard for her to reconcile as she realized that she'd lost spaces of time that she'd never recover. She missed the early development of three of her four living children and when she came back from her own private hell years before expecting to find Brenda Sue there and that she would still be an infant. Instead, she was mother to a baby boy. Larry's light colored hair reminded her of a baby she'd held for a few short weeks, a baby who left her. When she returned this time, Eddie was half-grown and she was faced with the reality that nobody's life had stopped but her's and her father's.

Across the Footbridge

Now, Pappy was gone too. How could he have left her? Sometimes she wished he'd taken her with him. There were days when she longed to go with him. He had been there when Peggy Ann went to the hospital and was there the day the doctor said she'd be okay. Months turned into years in the space of time that followed, time that robbed her of her father. How it all frightened her. She'd missed so much that sometimes she wished she could go back to the other hell. At least there she didn't suffer the pain she did here. Every day when she woke it was staring her in the face, the fear she felt inside reflected in the eyes of her family.

Eddie remained with Liphee and Paul but he came across the bridge with Larry each day when they returned from school. Sometimes he stayed till after supper, occasionally till bedtime. She longed to take back her rightful place in his life. He was her firstborn but she'd lost her right to him through the years. She had left him too many times and couldn't promise him that she wouldn't leave again.

On the second Monday in January, Ginny stood on the front porch watching Larry cross the bridge and walk the path to Liphee's back door. After he disappeared inside she closed the door against the winter air and returned to bed. Mondays were not her best days. Slipping under the covers she thought of her mother's words from the night before.

Maggie had finally found the strength to leave her bed after years of confinement. She was still blind so someone always led her across the bridge that separated her daughters' houses. The day before Larry led his grandmother into the kitchen where Ginny and Ben sat with a jug of wine on the table that separated them. Ginny knew that her mother couldn't see the wine so it must've been her slurred speech that revealed her secret. Maggie's words echoing through the house were tinged with anger.

"Ginny, what would your daddy say if he could see you now?"

She knew in her heart that her daddy would never see her drunk. If he had lived, she'd never started drinking in the first place because he would not have allowed it.

Now she lay on the bed, listening to the ache in her head as she tried to recall when she first started drinking. Pappy and George and Ben had always drunk wine and beer when they could afford it. Ben even ran moonshine when they were first married. She'd never thought about it till after Pappy died and Ben told her to try a little wine to see if it would calm her nerves. She had and it did. At first nobody else knew that she was drinking. It'd been difficult to keep the secret once she started drinking more than a drink or two to calm her nerves. She'd discovered that for a few hours she could take away a lot of the pain and most of the memories that continued to torment her.

A few weeks ago she started going to Ohio with Ben on paydays. The part of Kentucky where they lived was dry. If you crossed the bridge in town you could be in Ohio in a few minutes. On Friday afternoons and evenings, the bridge was packed with people going across the state-line to buy beer and wine to bring back to Kentucky.

Before Ginny's headache disappeared or sleep removed her from it, she heard the sounds of Roger rustling the covers on the bed across the room. Throwing the covers back, she

Across the Footbridge

rose from the bed where Peggy was still sleeping. She should get up and start the wash.

The Maytag washer that Ben bought a few months before was on the little porch off the hall behind the kitchen. He purchased the refrigerator at the same time. The man who owned the houses Ben and Paul paid rent on also owned a furniture store in town and he sold Ben the new appliances on payments. Ginny had never had anything new in any of the homes that she and Ben established through the years.

Every Monday, when she went to the back porch to start her weekly wash, the tub of the washer and the galvanized rinse tub were already filled with water. Ben bailed the water out of the well by the back door and filled both tubs on Sunday evenings. She spent most of Monday washing and hanging the clothes on the line, filled with appreciation for the agitator that did the work she used to do with her hands and a washboard.

Every Monday, supper consisted of the pot of beans that simmered on the back of the coal stove in the kitchen. In the afternoon she would stir a bowl of cornmeal and water and pour it in an iron skillet that held sizzling bacon grease. The cornbread would be cooling on the back of the stove when Ben returned home from work. The steam would still be rising from the bread when Ginny unhooked the drain hose and laid it at the edge of the porch to drain another week's worth of dirt back into the yard.

The house consisted of four small rooms. Each spring the owner supplied his tenants with paint and wallpaper. The front room had two windows overlooking the creek and there was a window in each of the other rooms. Painted woodwork surrounded every window and inside doorway. Ginny washed the woodwork each spring when she and Liphee replaced the paper on the walls. For years this had been an annual event, as were the two gardens she and Paul planted. The path separating the bridge from Paul and Liphee's back door also separated the gardens. Ginny and Paul always rivaled for the first and largest produce of the season.

At eleven a.m. June 3, 1958, the temperature had climbed to eighty-seven degrees. The sounds of kids playing mingled with the sound of a hammer's constant pounding on a roof three houses away. Larry found a quarter under the bridge in front of the house and today was his sister's fourth birthday. He made a mature decision to buy her a birthday party with his newfound wealth.

The hot morning sun had brought the freckles on his nose out to stand at attention when he stood in front of his mother and pleaded for permission to go to the store on the corner. Ginny was at the clothesline holding a pair of Ben's workpants in her hands and two clothespins in her mouth.

"Can I, Mommy? I know the way as many times as Eddie took me there."

"Larry, why can't you wait till your brother gets home to walk with you?"

"Cause...I only found a quarter. If I have to split the pop and tater chips four ways then there won't be enough for any of us."

"Okay, you can go if you promise to watch for cars and share whatever you get with Roger."

"Do I have too? It ain't his birthday...an' I found the money."

Across the Footbridge

"You heard what I said!"

Twenty minutes later, Larry wiped the spit off the pop bottle his sister handed him and took the second drink before he passed it to Roger.

"You know what Peggy Ann? You ain't never had a birthday party before!"

The bridge sheltered the three kids from the hot rays of the midday sun. A small yard separated the bridge from the hill that started at the back of the house and climbed towards the sky before it leveled and started to slope in the opposite direction. The sides of the hill were thick with trees, berry briars, and openings in the rock formations sticking out from its top. There was a large tree standing at the entrance of the tangled mess that covered the side of the hill that had become a part of the children's lives.

The tree was the place that the unlucky child hid his or her eyes and counted to ten, frontward and backward, while the rest ran and hid. The tree was base when a game of tag was in progress and the backside of the tree held the secrets of each child at one time or another. It provided the acorns that Peggy used in her baking of clay biscuits and had been Larry's hiding place when things that he saw or heard frightened him.

After Peggy's birth, he witnessed his mother doing things and saying things that his young mind couldn't understand. The adults surrounding him didn't hold the answers so he was left to draw his own conclusions. He spent many hours on the hillside behind his house as fear of his mother drove him into hiding. Ginny held no knowledge of the fear her actions planted in him and he didn't have the maturity to understand that the person he was afraid of wasn't his mother, but was a shell that the disease left in her place when it removed her from him.

In the fall of 1958, Roger boarded the school bus with his two older brothers while Peggy stood beside Ginny on the front porch. They watched the boys cross the bridge that'd take them to Liphee's house and the bus stop in front of it. Peggy was four years old and memories of her years with Liphee and Paul were fading.

Ginny cared for her home and family and shared hours of idle chatter with Liphee during the long afternoons. Liphee and Paul had hope for another pregnancy the year before, only to be disappointed again with another miscarriage. They both continued to treat their niece and nephews as their own children. Eddie had returned to live with his parents the previous winter but he continued to divide his time between the two houses.

Another mineshaft had opened and this time the vein of coal would provide work for Ben for two years. He kissed Ginny on the front porch each morning before the first tinges of dawn crept into the sky then drove eight miles to the site where he entered the shaft before the sun rose. Peggy hid behind the door in the mornings to witness the goodbye kiss that was the only expression of her parents' affection that she would ever see. As time passed, the family grew away from the pain and horror that'd surrounded them for so many years.

On a bright August morning in 1960, Peggy stood in front of Liphee's house with her brothers and waited for the school bus. Standing at Liphee's front door, Ginny watched the bus remove her last child and take her into a world that she'd never seen. She returned to the house across the bridge that'd become silent.

The raised train tracks that ran parallel with the road in front of Liphee's house concealed the road on the other side. If the tracks hadn't been there you could have seen the large white house from Liphee's. The family living in the house consisted of an elderly couple, their grown son, and a small dog. Once the neighbors became aware of the young children in the neighborhood, the lady of the house took upon herself the responsibility of taking the children to church, and befriending their mother.

Mrs. Melvin's hair was white and her lips were painted a bright orange. She spent part of each weekday afternoon sitting in Ginny's front room while Ginny mended Ben's workpants, or removed damp balls of clothing from the bushel basket parked under the ironing board. Every Sunday morning, Mrs. Melvin appeared at Ginny's door to claim any child inclined to go to church. She encouraged their inclination with Dentyne chewing gum, money for the collection plate and a few extra pennies for the child. Mrs. Melvin provided Ginny with gardening tips and a subject of conversation for the supper table. She was the first friend Ginny had made outside her family since she became ill as a young girl.

Nineteen-sixty was a good year for the family. Mary had grown into a woman in the space of time since Charley died and that year Maggie received the first social security check issued to her and that fall she moved to a nicer house a mile down the road. George still worked at the cemetery and Ben's work at the mines remained steady. Paul and Liphee were expecting another baby in the spring. This pregnancy

Across the Footbridge

endured past the critical first three months. Liphee spent part off each day with her feet elevated and her optimism growing with the life that continued to mature inside her.

The weekends had taken on a routine of their own beginning on Friday afternoon when Ben and Ginny made their scheduled trip across the bridge. By Friday night, the kids were all tucked into beds at Liphee's house and Paul was sitting at the table in Ginny's kitchen, arguing politics or religion with her and Ben. By Sunday afternoon, Friday night's conversation was occasionally brought up and rehashed by the three adults as they started their weekly trip back to sobriety.

On Monday mornings, the weekend was dismissed from everyone's thoughts as they dealt with the beginning of a new week and the remnants of headaches. Liphee learned that the best way to deal with the other adults during the weekly drinking spree was not to deal with them. She kept the kids out of the way and waited out the two days that would bring order into both houses, come Monday.

On Mother's Day, 1960, the woman who'd cared for her sister's babies for so many years, held her own son in her trembling arms. Two months later Ginny told her that Ben wanted to move back to the country.

"Ginny, what'll happen if you get sick again?"

They didn't see the frightened seven-year-old standing under the kitchen window the day that they discussed the upcoming move. Peggy Ann knew that she shouldn't be listening to the conversation filtering through the screen that covered Liphee's open window.

Across the Footbridge

Ginny sat at the end of Liphee's kitchen table, a colicky baby riding face down on her knees as they swayed back and forth. Liphee was pouring the formula she'd just prepared into a row of sterilized bottles lined up on the table.

"Don't Ben know that Mr. Roberts won't make you all move just because you're behind on the rent again? He's got more money than he'll ever live to spend anyway!"

"He knows that. He said he wanted to move closer to his people, after all these years that we've never been close to 'em. It all started when we went to that reunion last month."

Peggy remembered the day her mother was referring too. There were tables filled with food and lots of people that her daddy told her were her relatives. She had a grandma and grandpa that she never knew until that day. Her Grandma Rice patted her face and gave her an apple and Grandpa Rice called her to come stand in front of him while he peered into her face. He said she reminded him of her mother. She stood in front of him waiting for him to dismiss her. His chin dropped to his chest while she stood there. Finally, a cousin that she'd never met walked by and told her that she could leave. She did and when she went back sometime later, he was still asleep.

Now, Peggy stood under her aunt's window trying to imagine what it would be like to live somewhere else.

That night, she lay awake wondering what her mother and aunt had meant about her mother getting sick again.

The last weekend in August, Ben loaded the back of his old truck and headed for the county highway that would take him to the house he'd rented at the end of a holler. It was late Saturday evening before he tied the last piece of furniture on

Across the Footbridge

the bed of the truck. He and Ginny had been drinking most of the day and before the truck was packed she decided that she wasn't going to make the move with him. The faces of four children showed their relief about the news but by the time the sun dropped behind the house she had changed her mind. The kids didn't change theirs back when she did and Liphee informed Ben and Ginny that they could return for their children the next day, if they were both sober. Sunday, Liphee informed Ginny that she'd had her last weekend binge. She wouldn't be living next door to her and able to care for the kids anymore.

Across the Footbridge

Chapter Ten

The truck followed the highway past the county high school and at the next intersection it turned west onto a road leading into the adjoining county. Fifty minutes had passed since Ben headed the old truck out of Liphee's driveway when he steered it towards the dirt road that'd lead them to the door of their new home. The boys riding in the back of the pickup watched civilization fade as miles were put between the last home they'd known and the one they would soon see for the first time. Peggy Ann perched on the seat between her mother and father as she looked over the dashboard at houses that became further apart. Ben told her that she just passed the

93

one-room school she would start second grade in next week. It was the same school he attended when he was a boy. She tried to imagine being in the same classroom with both of her brothers, and couldn't.

The dust from the road leading them into the holler rolled over the cab of the truck swirling around Larry and Roger's faces and filling their eyes and noses with grit. There was only one other house between the paved road and the house where the truck stopped. The dust was just beginning to settle on the road behind them as the boys climbed down from the back of the truck.

The driveway where Ben parked was a bed of flattened weeds. The only other indication of life was the tracks he made in the weeds in front of the house when he brought their furniture and unloaded it, the tall growth between them and the front door parted from his numerous trips to and from the truck. His brother's boy had shown up early that morning to see if they'd gotten moved and he had helped Ben unload the truck and set up the beds before Ben and Ginny returned to Liphee's to pick up the kids. Eddie had refused to move with them. He wanted to finish his schooling with the class at the county high school.

That morning, the three kids stood beside the old truck trying to see their new home over the tops of weeds that were taller than they were. Ben borrowed a sickle from his brother and within an hour there were paths cut to the front door and the outhouse that'd before been invisible. The boards on the front porch gave with the weight of one adult or two kids. The house consisted of three dark rooms, the inside retaining the odor of years of abandonment. Ginny opened the front door early that morning hoping to entice some of the sunlight inside. There was a tiny window in the kitchen but with weeds growing halfway up the house, little air filtered through the torn screen covering it.

After Ben cut the path to the outhouse, he connected the stovepipe in the kitchen and built a fire so Ginny could prepare their first meal in their new home. She cautioned Peggy about going to the outhouse alone, telling her that the stalks the sickle left in the yard would be a good hiding place for snakes. The noises surrounding the house that night kept Ginny and three kids awake long after the sounds of Ben's snoring were heard.

The first week the family spent in the little shack seemed to take a lot of adjusting from everyone, except Ben. He left the house each morning at daybreak and returned late in the afternoon with a look of contentment shining through the coal dust that covered his face. Larry and Roger explored the woods and hills during the days while Ginny struggled to find space in the small rooms for their belongings. By Friday, the family was familiar with the house and surroundings and on Saturday afternoon they received their first company.

Liphee parked the car in the flattened weeds. The weed stalks that'd been cut down the week before had dried into three-inch high spikes that poked at the openings in her sandals as she made her way to the front door. The red dust from the road carried with the breeze towards the open door, the gritty particles reaching the doorway before she and Eddie did. They both stepped on the porch at the same time and the sound of old wood splitting was their first greeting. Liphee found her way around the rotting boards to step into her sister's front room. The old television set that Paul gave the kids the year before was setting on top of a chest of drawers. A double bed took up most of the remaining space in the little room.

"Ginny, where's your front room furniture?"

"Ben had to put most of it in the old barn at the back of the house."

Liphee laid the burden of her sleeping son in the middle of the bed but Eddie remained outside. She could see his back and hunched shoulders from her perch on the edge of the bed.

"How's Ben and the kids settling in?"

"They're doing all right. The kids start school Monday, and Ben is as happy as a coon in the hen house. I dread next week when the kids'll be gone during the day."

"You understand why Eddie stayed on with me and Paul, don't you?"

"Yea... I know he don't wanna start at another high school with only two years left. I've even thought about leaving Ben and going to stay with Mommy until he finishes his schooling."

"Ginny, are you gong to be all right up here in the end of this holler by yourself after the kids go to school?"

"Now, don't you go home worrying about me and the kids. I'll be alright, besides, you've already done all ya can fer us."

Liphee called for Eddie an hour later and he walked around the side of the house as she and Ginny reached the front of the car.

"Mommy, do you think Dad'll ever move back closer to town?"

Across the Footbridge

"I don't know Eddie. Will you come some weekend and stay all night with us?"

The dust from the car tires rolled back over the front of the house where Ginny stood, tears rolling down her face. In the car headed out of the holler, a baby was the only one making noise. Liphee and Eddie were lost in private thoughts.

Eddie was trying to justify his decision to remain with his aunt and uncle and civilization. It was true that he wanted to graduate with the class that his friends were in but he knew there was more to it than that. He didn't think he could stand being buried at the end of another holler and he couldn't spend every day and every evening sitting home remembering things that still tormented him from the past. He still thought about the years that he'd been hungry for days on end, times when his father was not around. He remembered the time they'd stayed with Aunt Arissa and he'd thought Pappy was going to die. He could remember the look in Pappy's eyes each time Liphee removed his bandages.

When his daddy showed up almost two months later, he'd wondered what took him so long. He knew where he spent his time cause he'd seen him with his girlfriend once. He'd pretend to be asleep sometimes late at night and hear Pappy and Grandma talk about her, and the other things. Sometimes it was hard for Eddie to be in the same room with his father, never sure where the anger he felt was coming from, but knew that he always felt it when he was around his dad.

Liphee steered the car out of the holler, her mind on other times. What would happen if Ginny got sick again? She'd done real well the last four years and other than that one time, she'd only gotten sick when the kids were born and Ben knew that they shouldn't have any more kids. She just hoped that he remembered to do something about it. It had been different when Pappy was alive. He seemed to know when Ginny was at risk of being hurt or doing something to harm herself. With him gone and Ginny so far away from the rest of the family, Liphee wasn't comfortable with any part of the situation. She wondered what would happen now that Ginny couldn't drink with Ben on the weekends. By the time the car pulled onto the pavement, tears blurred her vision of the road. The only passenger unaffected by the visit was the baby Eddie held in the front seat. Bubbles of spit grew from the wet mouth that continued to carry on a babbling conversation with the dashboard.

Monday morning, Ginny watched the kids out of sight then returned to the kitchen to pour the last of the coffee in her cup. It was washday. How would she ever survive the winter in this shack? The kitchen was so small that the table had to be pushed against a wall in order to have enough space to walk between it and the stove. The top of her kitchen cabinet set in the back room with the kids' beds because the ceiling was too low. How could Ben expect her to live like this, just so he could be closer to his people? He hadn't been over to see his folks all week anyway.

The school resembled a small church. The steps that led to the entrance were wide with railing on either side and part of the roof covered the small landing in front of the double doors. At exactly eight a.m. on school days, someone came to stand in front of the doors and wave a clanging bell. The first days of school after summer and Christmas vacations, the bell ringer was a middle-aged woman with a sweater draped over

Across the Footbridge

her shoulders. A gold chain was always visible at the front of her throat, keeping the sweater from slipping off her shoulders. No students were allowed inside the school before the sound of the bell, unless you were designated to hold a special position. The students chosen for these duties were rewarded with the tasks of bringing in water from the well behind the school, bringing in coal and small pieces of wood, and ringing the bell to signal that the other chores had been accomplished. The teacher made her favored choices for the following morning during the last hour of the school day.

The schoolyard consisted of a patch of mowed grass on one side of the building with a path worn down the middle leading to the two outhouses at the back of the lot. On the opposite side was a small playing field. Depending on the season, the field was used for baseball, red rover, basketball, or freeze tag. The colder the temperature outside, the more aggressive the sport became.

The inside of the building was divided into two spaces. The first area was a small room with coat hooks placed at various heights and benches placed against one wall. Another wall held shelves that were assigned spaces to hold brown paper bags and any toys that you didn't want to become the teacher's. This was also the designated lunchroom with the menu dependent on the contents of the brown bags the students carried from home.

The desks inside the larger room were divided into groups with each grade level a separate group. Peggy Ann was in the group of second graders. Roger was in with the fourth grade, and Larry with the fifth grade group. With no third grade students, the teacher taught seven classes. The first day's morning hours were spent in introductions and distributions of books. A lot of the thirty-one students were accustomed to out-door plumbing and the building of fires for warmth. Ben's nieces and nephews filled the majority of the seats in the upper grade classes. The teacher along with her students took turns drinking from the galvanized water bucket and making the necessary trips through the yard when nature called.

That afternoon, the kids returned from school to find their mother in a quiet mood. Ginny remained quiet throughout the evening and Ben felt the tension when he sat down to supper. He talked about his day as if the rest of the family was as happy as he was. By the end of the week, Ginny was talking to Ben again but he didn't like what she was saying.

"I can't spend the winter buried in the head of this holler! When the kids are at school and you're at work, I'm afraid to go to the toilet or clothesline cause I worry about snakes in the yard. I can't take it anymore! If you don't get me out of here... I'm taking the kids and going to live with Mommy!"

A pulse was visible at the corner of his right eye. He swallowed the food in his mouth with a sip of scalding coffee before he answered.

"Let me see about that house down the road. I heard today that the people who live there might be moving back to town. Would you like to move in there? It's closer to the main road, and there's a spot for a garden. I don't think it rents for much more than we're paying here."

Two weeks later, Ben moved his family into the other

Across the Footbridge

house and suddenly Ginny had more room than she had furniture. Her spirits lifted as she washed the windows in the big house and hung curtains. She even found a few overlooked vegetables in the garden behind the house that she packed into glass jars and stored away for the winter. When the kids came home from school the sounds of her songs usually greeted them. She sang as she took clothes down from the line or removed the iron skillet from the oven.

The rest of Ginny's family was going through transitions of their own that fall. Mary married, and Mag and George moved back into the house that Ben and Ginny had left. With Mary no longer at home to help with Maggie, George and Liphee shared the responsibility of their mother. He brought her home a puppy that soon learned to navigate for her as well as the grandkids had and within a few months the big shaggy brown dog could lead Mag between her and Liphee's doors. Soon they were traveling as far as the corner store.

By the first snowfall of the season, they received news that Mary was expecting her first child and that the mine was closing. The large house became difficult to heat without the free coal that he used to haul home from the mine. He searched for work in the area and signed up to draw his unemployment benefits. The small amount he received twice a month covered the rent and electric bill with barely enough left to put gas in his truck and soon the vegetables that Ginny put back for winter were gone. The only food in the house was the surplus government food Ben hauled home from the county seat on the first Tuesday of each month. The county courthouse was responsible for the distribution of the government's surplus food to the needy families in the community and consisted of anything left over from the previous month's supplies. Some months, the surplus contained canned meat, butter, and peanut butter. Always, it contained dried milk and eggs, five-pound blocks of cheese, yellow cornmeal, and rice.

Ginny taught herself to make buttermilk from the powdered milk but the cornbread started coming out of the oven the same height as the dough it went in as. The government didn't supply baking powder and there was no money to purchase it with. The family ate rice every day and the months that the surplus contained meat became times to look forward to. During the later part of the winter, Mary spent the weekend with them. She did without as her sister did, and went to bed early as the family had become accustomed to, making fewer hours in the day to be cold and hungry.

Ben tried without success to find work in the area and by March knew that he would be returning to the cemetery to work. When school was dismissed for the summer, he loaded the family's possessions on the truck and moved back into civilization. The new house wasn't much better than the one Ginny refused to live in the year before but it had four rooms, and was in the right school district. Eddie returned to live with his mother.

A pen at the back of the house contained enough mud to fill the spaces between the logs of a good size house, two feeding troughs, a galvanized wash tub full of water, and three hogs the family fed in order to receive a discount on the rent. The landlord had an old trailer parked in front of the house

Across the Footbridge

where he stored feed for the hogs. Ben and the boys removed bags of cornmeal and boxes of powdered milk from the trailer to throw in the pen each day. Peggy watched the hogs devour the same food that'd kept her family alive a few months before. At eight years of age she came to understand that some people had, and some people had more.

The house was only a mile from town but it too was at the end of a dirt lane. When the fall rains came, the road became a rutted field of slippery red clay. Ben's old truck held the mud from the road through the winter until the spring rains came and washed it clean. The tires coated the sides of the truck with each trip it made in and out of the holler.

Eddie had one year of high school to complete. He took a job at a store at the edge of town, saved his money and bought an old car. The mechanic's class he enrolled in at the vocational school taught him the necessary skills he needed to keep his junk heap rolling down the roads.

A year later another mineshaft was opened. Ben returned to the mines and moved the family to another house. During the year that followed they moved two more times. Ben continued to find housing within the school district and Eddie remained at home.

The teenager was looking forward to graduation. He would be the first in his family to receive a diploma and that spring his spirits soared as time drew near for the graduation ceremony. Who would be there to share in the pride of his accomplishment when he assembled with his classmates for the last time?

"Ginny, don't you want to go and see Eddie receive his diploma?"

Across the Footbridge

"It's not that I don't wanna'. I don't have anything to wear...an' I know I can't find my way around that big school by myself. Why don't you go in my place? It'll be as good as me being there."

The air was warm and heavy from the rain of the night before. Eddie pulled his graduation robe on over the white shirt and black dress pants that Paul bought him the week before. Looking at his image in the mirror on Liphee's bedroom dresser he knew that he'd finally made it. He had looked forward to this day for so many years. He'd always known that he would break away from the poverty that his family had struggled in for what he thought had been forever, and from the time that he was just a kid he'd noticed that the people who had the things that his family didn't also had an education, something else that his family members had been lacking. So from the time he'd been in third grade he'd been looking towards today. He didn't want to work himself into an early grave as Pappy had then die with as little as he started out with. Eddie had promised himself that he and his would never know the pain of hunger.

Tomorrow, he would start working at the dry-cleaners in town. He was hiring in to wash shirts, but he planned on looking for a better job right away.

"Eddie, it's time to leave!"

When he walked into Liphee's kitchen, he almost didn't recognize the woman standing by the door. Once he did, he felt a rush of pride enter somewhere deep in his gut and swell upward to fill his chest cavity.

"Mommy, you look great!"

Across the Footbridge

Liphee'd found a suit, hose, and shoes that fit Ginny as well as if she had shopped for them herself. Ginny felt as different as her family assured her she looked and the pride she felt sitting in the gymnasium that night flushed her cheeks and lit sparks of lights in her eyes. She sat among the other parents and listened as the potential future of her son was presented to her through the words of the ceremony's speakers. For the first time in her life she realized that her children's generation didn't have to live as all of the ones before it had. Her son had a chance for a different future.

1*Across the Footbridge*

Chapter Eleven

November 22, 1963

Ginny turned the television on before she went to the back yard to fight a biting winter wind while she filled the line with wet clothes. She returned to the kitchen and poured the leftover coffee in a cup and carried it and a pair of Ben's workpants that needed mending to the front room. It was time for the soap operas. When she watched the lives portrayed on the small screen she forgot her own for a while. At first she thought the commotion on the TV was part of a new plot that she'd missed when she'd been in the back yard.

She watched the man on the screen with tears rolling down his cheeks inform her and the rest of the nation that their

106

Across the Footbridge

president had just died. The same fear that had been part of her life for more than twenty years widened to encompass a young woman in a pink suit that a camera exposed to a saddened nation.

Peggy Ann was pondering the thirteenth question on a History test when the principal's voice interrupted the silence. All eyes immediately turned towards the intercom mounted above the teacher's desk. The test in progress was forgotten with the somber announcement. Mrs. Eastland cradled her head in her upturned hands as waves of shock and grief racked her body. Thirty-one frightened nine-year-olds watched from their seats as their teacher mourned the death of a young man who'd just died in Dallas.

For five days, the low drone of a newscaster's voice could be heard in the background while the image of a young woman with bloodstains visible on her suit continued to move through Ginny's head. Her heart reached out to someone who'd never known the pain of hunger and poverty, but now knew the devastation of loss as she did. Ginny saw Lee Harvey Oswald succumb to the firing of a gun on November 24. She had the same pair of pants lying in her lap that she'd been holding two days before when she'd learned of President Kennedy's assignation.

It was the first time the kids could ever recall their parents' conversation at the supper table being dominated by an event that hadn't occurred within the family. As a nation mourned the events of the history being made, no one knew the direction that a president's death would turn their lives in. A week later the schools reopened their doors and the soap operas again picked up the plots from the week before.

Meanwhile, a small country across an ocean was moving towards the devastation that would eventually penetrate the walls of a small house in Eastern Kentucky and touch the lives of people in it, people who were unaware of its existence.

Eddie was still washing shirts. Mary discovered that she was pregnant when her daughter was seven months old. She struggled to care for her baby with another growing inside of her. That struggle was combined with one to save a failing marriage. Ben found another house to move his family to and Larry was getting impatient to follow in his older brother's footsteps. He too, was eager to leave his parents' home and the poverty of their lifestyle. Liphee and Paul's baby had grown to be a boy who traveled the path to the bridge that led him to his grandmother's house on the other side. As the nation struggled in its adjustment to the tragic loss of its leader, Mary was adjusting to the death of her marriage. She moved back into her mother's house when her second daughter was three weeks old.

George hung his shovel on its nail at quitting time and closed the door on the shed for the last time. He gave his boss notice the week before that today would be his last day but he still had to tell his family. He thought about the people he'd soon leave on his last walk home from the cemetery where his father was buried.

He'd often thought about just walking away and had always yearned to see places with names that he struggled to pronounce. Now it was time for him to see what the world was like away from the family that had made up his world for thirty-seven years. He might not get another chance to leave.

He wanted to leave home when he first became of age

but he stayed on to help with Ginny's kids and help Pappy try to keep everyone fed. Then Pappy died, and about the time he'd been ready to leave, Mary got married so he stayed to help take care of his mother. He remembered the day he found the pup behind the shed at the cemetery. The little guy was looking for its mother's belly and had nuzzled George's neck looking for a source of food. He carried him home in his jacket pocket and told his mother he'd found her a seeing-eye dog.

Now that Mary was back home to look after their mother, he was going to leave before something else happened. He'd signed up to join a crew leaving for Ohio the following morning. He'd pick tomatoes for a soup factory until the season was over. If he didn't like being away from home, he would come home then.

Mary watched George's back as he crossed the bridge the next morning. Maggie was quiet, thinking of the young man who had always reminded her of Charley. George wasn't as big a man as his dad had been, but he had the same black curly hair and the same smile. She'd asked him the night before why he didn't just find a wife and settle down, maybe have a couple of kids.

"Mommy, I've had kids. I sat up nights rocking Ginny's babies and I hurt when they did, and I've suffered with the rest of you the days those kids did without. I watched them learn to walk and talk, and I've thought about doing it with kids of my own. I don't think I could stand to watch more kids go through what I've seen those go through and not be able to do anything about it. Besides, a man like me doesn't need a wife. I like to drink, and I don't want a woman telling me that I shouldn't. I'll either call or have someone write for me occasionally, so you'll know where I'm at."

George used the bus ticket the man from the employment office gave him the week before and when the Greyhound pulled out of the station he was sitting in the seat behind the driver.

One of the women who worked at the dry-cleaners took notice of Eddie the first day he started working there. A few weeks later, she asked her daughter to stop by the business to drop off some things she'd forgotten to take with her. After Becky handed the bag to her mother and left the building, Eddie walked across the space that had separated them.

"Was that girl you were just talking to your daughter?"

Becky's mother casually mentioned that her daughter bowled every Friday night at the alley west of town. Three months later, Liphee told Ginny that she thought Eddie was getting serious about Becky.

A letter had arrived addressed to Maggie the month before informing her that George was headed to Florida to pick fruit. Mary's divorce was final the same day that Liphee's son, Michael, celebrated his fourth birthday with cake and ice cream. The evening news was filled with reports from a country in Southeast Asia.

The first time that Eddie had showed up at the bowling alley and asked to drive Becky home, she refused because her father was driving out to pick her up.

"If you think you'll be here next week, I'll tell Mom and Dad that I'll be riding home with you."

Eddie's car had been seen at the bowling alley every

Across the Footbridge

Friday night since. Becky was waiting to meet his folks. Her family greeted him warmly when they were introduced. Eddie didn't talk much about his family. She knew that his folks lived out in the country and that he stayed with his aunt and uncle. He told her that he had two brothers and a little sister that he'd introduce her to sometime.

They'd been dating for five months the afternoon Eddie entered the door to the big building downtown. When he left less than an hour later, he knew he'd have to tell his mother his news himself. Five days later he would report to the bus station and board a bus that'd take him to North Carolina. He was now a Marine.

He received his notification the day before. He'd known for a while that it was just a matter of time till his number was called but he still felt the shock when he opened the letter, his personal invitation to serve his country.

He'd watched the news during the last year as the United States' involvement in the crisis between the two small countries, escalated. On March 8, 1965, the first U.S. ground troops landed at DaNang. Paul had told him that evening that a lot of lives would be sacrificed before the conflict was resolved. Now, he faced the possibility that one of those lives might be his.

His feelings on the situation were mixed. He could identify with the horror some of his friends had already left to view first hand and he'd heard the tales of the heat and poverty of the two countries that were pitted against each other. The heat he could relate to because he'd spent months behind the presses that belched hot steam in his direction with each shirt that was pressed. The thought of doing without reminded him of his childhood. He knew what it would be like to dig a hole to eliminate body waste in, and the thought of going to sleep with his stomach asking for food was not going to be a new experience to him. These were the words of warning the recruiter said to him in the building he'd just left. The one thing that he wasn't prepared for was the thought of taking another person's life. The sergeant had told him that it would become second nature to him, once his own life was at stake.

Eddie's head was filled with the details he'd need to attend to before he boarded the bus the next Wednesday. He headed the car into the Friday afternoon traffic and followed its flow towards the highway that'd take him to the last house his father had rented. During the thirty-five minute drive, he thought of his mother and the shack that she had made into another home.

Eddie still hadn't found the courage to take Becky to his parents' home. He'd told her that they'd always been poor and she said that she understood, because her family had never had much either. He'd told her that his dad drank wine, and she said her dad did too. He hadn't been able to explain it to her, and so far he hadn't shown her what his parent's life was really like. It'd been more than a year since Eddie spent a night under his father's roof. Each time he went to visit his mother, he felt the helpless anger that her life always invoked in him.

He knew his dad spent money on wine that could have bought milk for the kids or shoes for his mother's feet. How did she stand it year after year, to just get by? He could remember the years after Pappy died when both of his parents drank. When they'd moved out in the country his mother stopped drinking. Afterwards, it was difficult to listen to the fighting that was always present on the weekends. After his mother stopped drinking, his dad started drinking her share. He was always passed out in a chair on Friday nights. How could he take Becky into that?

Eddie parked his car in front of the steps that led to the yard in front of his parents home. The house was four rooms long and one room wide. The front porch had been built on later, apparently. Whoever did the construction, forgot to build steps leading to it. Eddie passed the well in the back yard on his way to the kitchen door. The well was a length of pipe protruding about three feet above the ground. It hadn't produced any water in all the months his family had lived here. Ben hauled water for the kitchen in the back of his car in milk jugs and a five-gallon container while the rain barrel at the corner of the house provided water for washing clothes and baths. What water didn't run off the house and his dad didn't haul home in his car, Larry and Roger carried from a neighbor's house up the road.

Eddie opened the kitchen door and yelled for his mother as he moved through its opening. Ginny was in the back bedroom putting the last of her washing away when she heard him call for her. She hurried through the house towards the sound of his voice. Eddie was waiting for her when she entered the little kitchen.

"I'm glad I got here before Dad and the kids did. I've got something I want to talk to you about. Can I have a cup of coffee? I still miss your coffee."

She filled the old metal pot with water from a jug that

113

was on the sink. She put a hand full of coffee on top of the water, set the lid on the pot and pushed it towards the middle of the stove. Eddie waited for her to sit down before he told her that he wouldn't be back to visit for a while.

"I know when I get back... I'll be able to get that job at the refinery. I'm going to have to go sooner or later, and it's not so bad over there right now. Anyway, I'll be a lot better off being in the Marines than I'd be if I was just going into the army."

"Eddie, you'll be careful won't you? I don't want you to get over there and think about things here and get hurt."

"I'll be all right, and I'll be back before you know it."

Ben experienced a great deal of paternal pride for the fact his son was becoming a Marine while all that Ginny felt was fear.

In the three months that Eddie trained for survival in a jungle, his family counted the days till his service would be over. Peggy shared with her History class the news that her brother would soon be going to the war that was making the nightly news. Chet Huntley and David Brinkley shared the events in Vietnam with the nation five times a week and Ginny waited for the mail delivery each day, hoping a message from her son would be delivered.

Maggie had an appointment with an eye doctor in town who promised her the possibility of her sight. She underwent surgery on both eyes a month after Eddie left for boot camp. When the bandages were removed from her eyes the surgeon performed a test on her. He asked her daughters to line up at the end of her bed and after he removed the dressings he'd put on Maggie the week before, he asked her if she could see anything. Slowly, her eyes adjusted to the light, and then focused on the three women standing at the end of her bed. The doctor asked her if she recognized anyone.

Pointing to Liphee, she said, "That's my oldest girl, Ginny."

She then pointed to Mary with an introduction of Liphee, and looking towards Ginny, told the doctor, "and, that's my baby girl, Mary."

The surgeon chuckled as he left the three daughters to reintroduce themselves to their mother. Seven weeks later when Eddie returned from boot camp, Maggie looked at a man standing in front of her who would replace the image of a boy she'd retained for more than fifteen years.

Larry turned fifteen that spring, the last two years seeming like ten to him. Things were okay during the week, but come Friday, he knew that he'd be in a fight before sobriety and Monday morning arrived. He couldn't understand what it was that always triggered a fight with his dad and every week he told himself, this weekend he'd just keep quiet and let whatever his dad said, pass. He always broke his promise sometime Saturday.

Ben used the quickest access known to him if he wanted to get back at Ginny. His denial of Larry was a knife that cut her deeply and the destruction of his relationship with his son. He had never doubted his paternity of Larry because the boy took after his side of the family more than any of the other kids, except Brenda. That was the real spark that always set him off. Larry reminded him so much of the baby they lost that when he was little Ben could hardly stand to look at him.

Across the Footbridge

By the time his older brother was in boot camp, Larry was spending the majority of his weekends at his grandmother's house. That was the only way he'd found to avoid the weekly battles at home. When he could, he was going to quit school and find a job in town.

Eddie returned home for two weeks after boot camp. The boy, who went east three months before, returned home with the body of a man. Peggy stared up at the stranger standing in her mother's kitchen, the sight of her brother in uniform appearing unreal to her.

When Maggie looked at him, her heart made the same swirling dip it'd done all those years ago.

"Eddie, you're the image of your grandpa the first time I laid eyes on him."

He drove Becky home from the bowling alley the last Friday that he was home.

"When I get back, I want to take you out to see my mom and dad. Can we get married after my tour is over?"

Eddie flew to San Francisco the next day. From there, he connected with other young men who were crossing an ocean to spend thirteen months in hell. Becky had written eleven letters before she received an address to send them to.

Ben was struggling each day at the mine. The shovels filled with coal had grown heavier in the last year and the pain in his back and shoulders now persisted through the weekends. Each morning, he picked up the pick to chisel more coal from the walls of the mine and struggled with the knowledge that his days as a miner were numbered. He returned home in the evenings to sit in a chair in the kitchen, while Ginny washed away the layer of black coal dust from his face and hands before he ate his supper. He was asleep before dark in the chair in front of the television.

The wine that he consumed on the weekends was the only thing that numbed the pain. Some weeks, he didn't make it till Friday. There was a little store a few miles up the road. The shelves in the store were stocked with bread, milk, pop, and candy. The shelves in the backroom held bottles of wine and beer that the owner sold to a select group. The group consisted of anyone in the area who cared to pay the price of illegal booze. Before the first letter from Vietnam arrived, Ben was making the trips to the little store almost every day. The same day that the first letter from overseas arrived, the boss informed the men that Friday would be their last day. The vein of coal was depleted and with the new regulations there wouldn't be another shaft opened in the area. The trend would now be to strip the tops of the hills and remove the vein of coal before the hill was restored. The large companies had succeeded in their plans to eliminate the small mining industry.

Ginny had watched the mailbox every day for the last three weeks. Each day that the carrier stopped in front of the house, she brought whatever was in the box inside. She was sure that the different colored stripes on the envelope meant that Eddie's first letter from the war had arrived. She placed the envelope on the kitchen table and waited for someone to come home and read it to her.

She heard the squeak of the brakes before she saw the yellow top of the school bus. All afternoon, she'd returned to the table where she'd placed the envelope, praying that it contained words from Eddie. She always turned the television on first thing in the mornings and watched the news reports of battles taking place in the strange country with a name she struggled to pronounce. She held her breath each time a camera depicted a scene of a combat zone, afraid that she'd recognize one of the faces flashing across the screen.

Peggy entered the house before her brothers and Ginny held the envelope towards her.

"This is from your brother, ain't it?"

Chapter Twelve

"Don't you go putting your hands into anything you don't know what is!"

The voices of the two drill sergeants continued nonstop through eighteen hours of every day. The new issue of supplies had included steel-soled jungle boots, lightweight poplin fatigues and heavy weight army-green socks. Piled into heaps at the feet of each private were tubes of black face paint, insect repellent, ponchos and liners, camouflage underwear, and their malaria pills. The sergeant continued on with his weeklong spiel.

"The M-16 is an outstanding weapon, it'll save you and your buddy's ass. It will lose you yours, if you don't keep it clean! And remember, always keep two things dry, your weapon and your feet. You just think you've heard of jungle

Across the Footbridge

rot."

"No one, at No time, is too say anyone's name over any radio! Got that!"

"All the women that you will see around the villages have one of two things. They've got a weapon, or they've got the clap. Which would you rather receive from them?"

For seven days the boys who'd spent three months preparing to come here, were instructed in how to get out of here, alive. Each night, the new recruits fell asleep with the sergeants' voices still rambling through their heads. *"How would they tell the enemy from the ally when they both looked the same?"*

Eddie carried a pad of paper and ink pen that he'd been issued the day before behind a shack at the back of the mess tent. He tried to erase the horror of the last week from his mind before he wrote his first letters home from Vietnam.

Dear Mother,

I'm finally getting settled. This is the first chance that I've had to write since we landed. We've had orientation all week and we're supposed to move out sometime next week. The weather here is real warm. This is supposed to be their winter. How is everyone there?

You can mail your letters to the address on the envelope. They'll bring our mail to us until we get set up in a more permanent spot. Things here aren't so bad, so far. The food is served in a tent by a bunch of the guys. I've only got a few minutes of free time left. I'll write when I can.

Your Son,
Eddie

Across the Footbridge

Eddie sat looking at the letter. It was hard to write and not tell her how things really were, but this was just the beginning. Each night the guys crossed one more day off the calendars that stood between them and home. He'd already heard the stories about the calendars that only had four or five days left, when the guy who'd marked all of those X's got to go home in a bag. He swiped at the bugs and sweat on his face with the same motion. If this was winter... he could hardly wait for summer. Eddie folded the letter to his family and sealed it in an envelope then started one to Becky.

Dear Becky,

I'm sorry I haven't been able to write sooner. This is the first free time we've had since we got here. There are two guys here that flew out on the same plane with me and we are sharing bunk-space. One of them is married. The other guy got engaged the same day that we did.

I wanted to tell you that in a couple of months we get a leave and I plan on buying your ring then. I'll ship it home to you as soon as I get it. If we get married when I get back to the states, do you think you'll want to stay with your mom until I finish up my stint? The way I've got it figured, it should only be about seven weeks.

How's things around there? Were your folks surprised when you told them our news? We've got to go out to Mommy's when I get back. I don't have much time left so I'll close for now. Use the address on the envelope unless I send you a new one. The sarg' said our mail will be trucked in to us twice a week with our supplies, but don't worry if you don't hear from me from time to time. Eventually, everybody's mail makes it back home (or so they tell me). I love you and I'm

121

Across the Footbridge

counting the days till.

All my love,
Eddie

Ginny and Becky received their letters the same day. Becky copied the new address onto the eleven envelopes she'd already sealed, before she started the letter that would reconnect her and Eddie.

Peggy dropped her schoolbooks on the kitchen table before she opened her brother's letter. After she read it to Ginny, she read it again to herself, trying to imagine the many miles that it had traveled in nine days.

"Peggy, did you bring home paper and pencil? I want to write to your brother after supper."

While Peggy was reading to her mother, her father was twelve miles away talking with the rest of the men who'd just lost their jobs. The owner had talked to each one of them that morning and when he walked out to the edge of the mine with Ben, he'd felt bad about the words he was obligated to say. The man that stood facing Ben was only half his age and Ben hauled coal for his dad when he and Ginny were first married.

"Ben, I feel worse about laying you off than I do all of the others. I know you really need the work. Have you thought about signing up for your disability? I know you've been drinking some during the day to help with the pain in your shoulder and back. Maybe... it's time you retired and took it easy."

Ben was the last miner to leave the site and at four o'clock he carried his hardhat and lunch pail home for the last time. On Monday morning, he left for the social security

122

Across the Footbridge

office in town and returned late in the afternoon with a slip of paper and a doctor's name and address he would see the following day. He asked Ginny if she wanted to stay at her mother's house while he went for his physical.

Maggie was crying and Mary's eyes were red and swollen when Ginny got there the next day. Maggie was holding the baby and the two-year-old was no where to be seen.

"Mary, why is Mommy crying, and where's Judy Ann?"

By the time Ben returned from his appointment, Ginny had been filled in on the events of the past three days. Judy Ann got sick on Friday and by Saturday night, her temperature was dangerously high. Early Sunday morning Mary called for her ex-husband to come and take them to the doctor. He arrived twenty minutes later, and soon they were racing towards the hospital. Judy Ann started convulsing before they reached the emergency room door. She was suffering from a severe case of bronchitis. The doctor prescribed antibiotics and she was going to be okay but would need to stay in the hospital a few more days, and her father wanted full custody of her. If she didn't agree, he planned on taking both of the girls. His exact words to Mary had been, "if you leave well enough alone, you'll get to keep the baby."

On Wednesday, Judy was released from the hospital and her father brought her to see her mother and grandmother before taking her to his youngest sister. His sister, who'd never been able to have children of her own, accepted the little girl as an answer to years of praying. Mary saved her child's life when she called for a ride to the hospital. She lost a daughter in the process.

Larry was counting the days until his birthday, only six more and then he could quit school. He'd skipped as many days this year as he could without the truant officer coming to talk to his dad. Now, he just wanted those last six days to pass. Every day that he rode the bus to school he'd only thought about how many hours it would be until he could ride it back home. He felt as if all of the kids at the high school were watching when he got off the bus. None of his clothes fit him and the pair of black high-top tennis shoes that he'd gotten last year had ruined his toes. He kept on wearing them after his feet grew too big for them and his toes curled into the toes of the shoes. Soon it would be over. He would be sixteen on Sunday and with any luck he would be able to find a job on Monday.

Roger was fourteen and Peggy was twelve. That's what Ben told the woman at the Social Security Office. She called him in to tell him he would receive his first check in a few weeks.

Larry rode the bus home with Roger and Peggy on Friday. He gave his brother the paper and pencil that he wouldn't need anymore. On Monday, he started washing shirts at the dry cleaners in town. He moved in with Maggie and Mary the same week.

Two weeks later, Eddie received the letter from his mother telling him his brother had dropped out of school and taken the job that he left. He wrote his reply the same day.

"Tell him to get his ass back in school before he ends up over here!"

It was two weeks before Ginny had the opportunity to

Across the Footbridge

deliver Eddie's message to Larry. There hadn't been money for food or gas for the old car till Ben worked one day for a man up the road who paid him in cash. He put gas in the car, bought a fifth of wine, and took Ginny and the kids to see Maggie and buy a few groceries. During the drive into town Peggy thought about the company that she'd had earlier that week.

That Monday was just like all the others till Peggy got off the school bus that morning and discovered that Janie was waiting for her.

"Can you go to my house?"

The Friday before, Janie decided that she wanted to be Peggy's friend and she bonded the friendship with the suggestion that they spend the night at each other's houses. Peggy had seen almost every girl in her sixth grade class bring an overnight bag to school at one time or another. She didn't bother to ask for permission to go home with Janie because she didn't own the required pajamas. Now, she was faced with the dilemma of taking Janie to her house, or trying to explain why she couldn't.

Peggy's heart began to race, filling her ears with the rushing noise of her heart pushing her blood through her veins and arteries. Seconds later, she tasted the sour heat of anxiety rising from her stomach. When the first bell rang, Janie followed Peggy into the school and down the hallway to their classroom. All morning Peggy watched the hands on the clock in the classroom move towards the time that she would have to take Janie home with her or tell her that she couldn't. Several times she tried to tell Janie that she couldn't have company but the words stuck in her throat, and then it was

125

time to go home.

With the sound of the last bell, Peggy retrieved her coat, books, and Janie, and started towards the line of buses beside the school. The small suitcase that Janie carried reminded Peggy of the night in front of them. The only luggage she ever saw at home was on the pages of the catalogs in the outhouse. On the ride home, she pointed out some of their classmates' homes to Janie. Peggy's voice became hoarse as her anxiety level increased with each stop that the bus made and all to soon, the squeaking brakes announced that it was time for Peggy and Janie to get off the bus. Janie kept up a constant stream of chatter as Peggy guided her up the rickety steps that ended at the edge of the yard.

The ground where they walked was rippled like a washboard from the heavy rains that washed off the hill behind the house. Peggy walked past the front porch that didn't have steps and skirted the rusty pipe sticking up from the red clay that made up the back yard. The pipe was the well that went dry several years before. Peggy stepped on the boards on the back porch that were the strongest and hoped that Janie would follow her tracks.

Peggy pushed on the back door and the two girls met the odor of cooked beans mingling with the hot sulfur smell of the coal stoves when they entered the kitchen. Ginny was standing at the stove pouring cornmeal batter into an iron skillet. The oven door was down and the rush of warm air brought a prickly sensation to their cold hands and cheeks.

"This is our kitchen," Peggy whispered as Janie's eyes took in her new surroundings.

The stove and the refrigerator that was empty most of

the time occupied one end of the little room. At the other end was one of the three windows in the house. At one side of the window was a painted wooden cabinet where Ginny stored her dishes and few baking supplies in the top with the bottom of the cupboard being home to pots and pans and canned food. At the other side of the window was a small sink. This was the most modern of their conveniences. It was here that the family disposed of all of the water they used. The wooden table in the middle of the room helped to conceal the worn linoleum underneath and a piece of oilcloth covered the top of the table. The table's shape was imprinted in the cloth with its pattern faded and edges beginning to show the wear of many scrubbings. Around the table were four chairs.

The yellow vinyl covering on the back and seat of Ben's chair was the only bright spot in the room. The worn smooth wood-grain of Ginny's chair was as familiar to Peggy as the features of her mother's face. This was the chair that her mother carried with her through her day. In the summers, she carried the chair to the shade of the front porch where she sat and snapped beans that she later put into Mason jars. She carried the chair to the back bedroom for privacy for her daily bath and this was the chair that she'd placed Peggy on for her baths when she was a small girl. She sat in the chair in the summer sunshine to rest, as her long black hair dried with the freshness of the outdoors clinging to it. Beside this chair was the one that someone had painted green and the other chair was missing its back. Peggy introduced Janie as they made their way into the next room.

"This is Janie…and she's spending the night."

If Ginny responded, Peggy didn't hear her, and she

didn't bother to look over her shoulder to receive a silent reply.

The small front room contained an old couch, a television that set on a black library table and the iron coal stove that took up the middle area of the room. Peggy led Janie through this room and lifted the quilt that hung between them and the space between two walls where she slept. This room was barely large enough to contain Peggy's half-size bed. The cold air on the other side of the quilt eliminated the need for Peggy to explain why they couldn't play there. The last room was even colder than Peggy's. The previous fall, Peggy helped Ginny tear their old clothes into strips and stuff them in the cracks around the window and the outside door in the back bedroom. The wind still whistled on occasion as it made its way inside to mock them in their efforts. This room held Ginny and Ben's old iron bed and the other bed where Roger now slept alone. The winter sun was filtering through the little window to make a streak of pale light on the dark patches of the heavy quilt covering Roger's bed.

Peggy explained the need to conserve the water in the five-gallon-can behind the kitchen door as she led Janie outside. Ginny remained silent when the girls passed through the kitchen the second time. After Peggy introduced her friend to the primitive plumbing, the cold March wind drove them back inside where supper was waiting.

Peggy and Janie perched side by side on the green chair, as Ginny ladled beans and cornbread onto their plates. The usual conversation was absent from the meal. Roger ate in silence, his eyes remaining on his plate. Ben and Ginny discussed the latest reports about the war while Peggy struggled to push her supper past the lump that'd formed in

Across the Footbridge

her throat early that morning. She washed her food towards her stomach with water, while she silently wished for more to offer her company. Janie finished her beans and thanked Ginny before she asked to be excused from the table.

"I hope you left room for desert."

At the back of the stove set an iron skillet. Inside, cherry juice bubbled along the edges of a brown crust. Peggy never knew where Ginny found the canned cherries and sugar she'd used to create the cobbler.

After the supper dishes were washed and put away, Peggy led Janie into the cold bedroom to get ready for bed. When she pulled the old clothes that she slept in out from under her pillow, Janie commented on the comfort of wearing old favorite clothes instead of pajamas to sleep in. Janie said goodnight to Peggy and her family, and was soon asleep. Peggy lay awake wondering what Janie would tell the rest of their class tomorrow.

Both girls woke when Ginny called Peggy's name. Ginny had used the last of her sugar and flour to make hot chocolate and biscuits. Janie thanked Ginny again as she headed out the door to catch the bus.

Some of the other girls were waiting in the parking lot when Janie and Peggy stepped down from the bus.

"What'd you have for supper?"

"Peggy's mother made cherry cobbler. It was awesome!"

As Peggy sat beside her mother on the ride to town almost a week later, she was filled with gratitude for the woman who'd made her friend feel special, and the friend who'd appreciated the effort. Several times that week her

Across the Footbridge

sentences had started with the words, 'My friend Janie'.

When Ben's car headed back towards the highway that afternoon, Larry stood in front of Liphee's house and watched it till it disappeared. He had listened to his brother's advice, delivered by their mother. They didn't understand, and he couldn't find the words to tell them. He had never found the niche at school that Eddie had. Eddie had been the oldest and the clothes he had were bought for him. Larry received the ones that Eddie outgrew. Eddie handed his books down to Larry. Eddie had always been good at studying and Larry struggled to receive good grades. And... Eddie was always gone when Larry heard the fights at home turn in his direction. Ben and Ginny returned home with two of their four children. Larry returned to his job washing shirts.

April6, 1966

Dear Eddie,

How are things with you? Your dad and I went to talk to Larry about his quitting school. I told him what you said. He said he knew what he was doing and that he'd be okay.

We heard from the Social Security about your dad's disability. They said the checks should start coming in a month or two. Junior took Judy Ann to live with his sister. Liphee is going to call a lawyer to see if Mary can get her back. He brought some kind of papers to Mommy's the other day and before he left he'd talked Mary into signing them. We'll let you know what happens.

The weather is starting to get warm and we'll be putting out a garden soon. We hope this letter finds you well and safe. I'll write again soon.

Your Loving Mother

Across the Footbridge

Becky marked off the days one at a time on the calendar that hung over her bed. She wrote to Eddie every day. Sometimes he received her letters six or seven at a time so she started numbering them so he'd read them in the proper sequence. In her last letter she told him that her sister was planning a bridal shower for her and she was going to invite Eddie's mother and sister.

April, 1966

The attorney informed Mary the divorce papers that she signed months before had in reality been papers relinquishing full custody of Judy Ann to her father. Judy's father waited for the proper time to execute his removal of his daughter from her mother's home, following the instructions of his lawyer. Mary hadn't had the money to retain an attorney. She still didn't.

Eight days after Mary received this information, Liphee and Paul were still discussing the issue and the probability of opposing it in court. When Paul left for work that morning, Liphee turned her attention to the windows she planned to clean that day. By one o'clock, the windows were cleaned and the lines in the back yard were filled with the weekly wash. She was planning Michael's fifth birthday party when someone knocked at the front door. She could hardly believe it, almost five years had passed since she first held her son in her arms.

She recognized the man on the other side of the screen-door. Paul had worked along side of him all the years that he and Liphee had been married.

Chapter Thirteen

May 2, 1966
Dear Eddie,
I'm sure that by now you've been notified of Paul's death. I am so sorry. I know that you loved and thought of him as a parent. Mom has been out to see Liphee a few times. There were a lot of people at the funeral. I wish I could have been with you when you received the news.

Love you always,

Becky

Across the Footbridge

Eddie folded the letter and put it back in his wallet. He was glad that she didn't question him about not coming home for the funeral. He really hadn't had a choice and was relieved about it. If he went home he wasn't sure that he'd have the discipline to come back.

He'd been in Nam for five months the day that he and four others returned from searching the scorched remains of a small village. The stench of dead bodies was still in his nostrils when the commanding officer motioned for him to wait up. The sergeant placed the Red Cross envelope in his blackened hands and walked away.

It took him an hour to muster up enough courage to open the telegram and find out who else had died. He was sitting at the back of the mess tent with the crumpled telegram clutched in his right hand when the guys who'd just returned from patrol with him passed and each man hesitated long enough to place a hand on his shoulder.

The man at Liphee's door three weeks before was Paul's boss. He drove her to the hospital filling her in on the details on the way. Paul and another postal employee had just returned from lunch when Paul complained of indigestion. The co-worker went to the medical department for antacids. When he returned a few minutes later he found Paul in a heap on the locker room floor. He called for assistance and someone summonsed an ambulance while Paul's supervisor came for her.

It felt like a dream and when she entered the emergency room fifteen minutes later a nurse was waiting for her. She was guided into a private waiting room. She didn't want to sit down as the nurse suggested. She wanted to see her husband.

"Please, just have a seat and the doctor will be right with you."

She knew as soon as she saw his face. It was in the eyes that refused to connect with hers. She saw the pity on his face and started to scream. The doctor yelled for a nurse and a hypodermic needle. Someone else called for Paul's brother to come to the hospital and pick up his widow.

Roger saw Liphee's stationwagon pass the house and turn around in the driveway of the next house before it returned to park in front of where he stood. He saw Liphee in the passenger seat, Mary in the backseat and a stranger behind the steering wheel and went to find his mother.

Ginny's knees started to buckle under when she saw Liphee's face. She'd lived in fear for five months anticipating one of two things. She waited for letters from Eddie or for a telegram informing her that there would be no more letters. It was Liphee's words that prevented her fall.

"He's gone, Ginny! Paul's gone ...an' I can't go on without him..."

A voice inside Liphee tried to reassure her that this was just a dream, some terrible nightmare that would fade into oblivion when she woke. Another part of her was above, watching the scene. That part saw the doctor inject the sedative and realized that once the drug wore away she would have to face the horrible reality. It was a nightmare from a feverish sleep. She was there, but only in form, not emotionally. Ginny saw the struggle going on inside Liphee and felt her own heart grow leaden with foreboding.

Across the Footbridge

"Paul was going to move some office equipment at work when he told the man with him that he was having pain in his chest and one of his arms. Then he collapsed. He died on the way to the hospital. When he left for work this morning he said that he'd be home at three. Ginny, what am I gonna' do?"

For so long she had been the strong one, the foundation that held up and sheltered the others. Now, she was crippled with grief.

The stationwagon pulled out a few minutes later with Ben's car following. Stung by the suddenness of Paul's death, Ben struggled with the reality of what had happened. Paul was a young man with a boy to raise. What was gonna' happen to him?

From the other side of the seat Ginny put his thoughts into words.

"What in the world is she gonna' do now?"

Maggie sat with Liphee's son, Michael, and Mary's baby while they went to Ginny's. Maggie was familiar with the pain surrounding her daughter. Sitting, waiting, she recalled the many times that she'd told her children just how painful this loss was.

"I've outlived both of my parents and I've buried a son, but nothing comes close to the pain of burying your daddy."

Her own words were coming back to haunt her. She knew from experience that the only thing that would ease Liphee's heartache was time, lots of time. She heard a car door slam in the driveway.

"Hi Mommy, where's everybody at?"

Across the Footbridge

"George! How on earth did you git home so fast? Liphee ain't even got home from tellin' Ginny and Ben about Paul. Who called you?"

Easing into the nearest chair, he asked.

"Liphee went to tell Ginny what about Paul?"

He'd started home two days before. He was sitting in a bus depot in Alabama waiting for a connection when a man asked him to help load some produce onto a truck a block from the station. The truck was headed for a town thirty miles north of George's hometown. He helped load the vegetables then returned to the ticket booth and cashed in his ticket. The truck driver paid for his meals on the trip home in return for his labor and companionship on the long drive.

"Why don't my daddy wake up?"

The words of a five-year-old tore through the adults gathered in his home two days later when Paul's body was brought home at three o'clock. She had him placed in front of the big window in the front room where he remained till the next morning. At that time he was taken to the cemetery down the road.

Her kitchen was close to overflowing with food and people. Every few minutes someone would go to answer a knock at the back door where another neighbor stood with a casserole dish or a can of coffee.

The front of the house was filled with Paul's brothers and sisters, standing in small groups, talking in hushed tones as they tried to come to terms with the death of their brother. Liphee was removed from both rooms with the assistance of the medication that the doctor sent home with her two days earlier.

Across the Footbridge

Two of Paul's brothers took her to make the arrangements at the funeral home and she appeared aloof. She knew that she was going to wake soon and the nightmare would disappear with the morning light. The medication failed her the next day when the flag was folded and placed in her trembling hands. She would never wake and find him beside her again.

The night of the funeral the brothers and sisters returned to their homes to pick up their lives where they'd left them three days before and she was left with the remains of three casseroles, a son that would be five years old in six days and a shattered soul. Two weeks later she received the insurance check that was her compensation for the man who would have held her for another fifty years.

Liphee packed the last box and George carried it out to the truck. Without looking back she closed the door on the house that she couldn't bear to live in anymore. For two weeks she'd seen him sitting at his place at the kitchen table in the mornings or walking in the backyard and every other place she turned her eyes towards.

The house where she moved was on the same road, only closer to town. The railroad tracks were still visible from her front door. The road on the other side of the tracks ran in front of the house that Maggie rented a few years before. The same week that Liphee moved into her new home, Maggie and Mary moved back into the house across the two roads and railroad tracks. Larry and George moved in with Liphee to help with Michael and a week later she started working at the dry-cleaners in town. She pressed the shirts that Larry washed.

Across the Footbridge

Liphee struggled to build a new life in the gaping hole that Paul's death left in her heart. The family that she supported now surrounded her. Maggie and George were there in the middle of the nights when she dreamed that it had all been a terrible mistake. She would wake and discover the empty space beside her and have to face reality again. He was gone.

She went to work six days a week and by Friday the week would have taken its toll on her. Every Saturday morning she drove to Ginny's with a small boy who was struggling as he attempted to accept his loss. His father was gone and his mother was changing. She returned to town, alone. Michael needed time away from her grief.

Ginny put her love in the void in Michael's heart that his father's death created. She included him in her every activity. He didn't see the poverty in her lifestyle, he saw adventure.

He was fascinated with building a fire with sticks and lumps of coal. He watched biscuits appear from a bowl instead of a can or bakery box. He was continuously amazed at the barrel at the corner of the house that never ran out of rainwater. He planted seeds and returned a week later to find green shoots in their place. Ginny cared for him as Liphee had cared for her children, with all of her heart.

The first disability check arrived and others followed with regularity. Without the need to be sober through the week Ben gave up the effort of trying. At the end of the month when the money was spent he began to charge his daily bottle of wine at the little store. The owner soon became familiar with his need to drink and the financial burden that it put on his family and offered him a job. The next week he became a bootlegger.

Six mornings a week he opened the little store and sold pop and candy to the children who occasionally rode their bikes past. In the afternoons and evenings he sold bottles of beer and wine to the adults that didn't want to make the drive across the river for a drink. With someplace to go each day he felt better than he had since the mine closed.

Weeks grew to be months and day by day Eddie marked off the squares on his calendar. He had changed in the ten months that he'd been crawling through the jungle. Remembering the bitterness that he took on the plane with him a year before he realized that it had been the poverty that he'd come to despise. Somehow he had come to hold his father accountable for much of the misery that he'd been exposed to. After a year of watching children beg for food while they had bombs planted under their clothing to blow up the obliging soldier that offered to feed them, he realized that his childhood, as bad as it was, could have been worse. The death and starvation that surrounded him here didn't have a chance for improvement. Most of the kids that didn't get blown up would end up dying from malnutrition. This must have been what his mother and father felt like. There wasn't a better future for them to look to. He planned on making a better life with Becky but his parents were living their future as he planned his. He started to understand that maybe his father didn't drink because he didn't love his wife and children. Maybe, he drank because he did. He ran away from them when Edie was small but he came back, and he stayed.

Across the Footbridge

The same days that brought Eddie closer to coming home were pushing Liphee into leaving. The small pittance she earned at the cleaners combined with her pension barely covered her and Michael's living expenses. Michael's needs would grow as he did and she refused to expose him to the poverty that was her childhood. Her sleepless nights became filled with thoughts of possible options. Realizing that she would need to relocate she kept her thoughts to herself till she was sure of her plans.

Eddie's last weeks in Nam were the roughest, and the longest. By then there were more than four-hundred-thousand American soldiers in the midst of the war. The increase in troops netted only more casualties. The service men were first to realize this. No matter how many villages that they took, another one was always in front of them. Some of their enemies turned out to be thirteen and fourteen year old kids. Along with the rest of his platoon, Eddie had long since given up the idea of winning. The main objective was to stay alive long enough to make it home. He was lucky. The two boys who flew across the ocean with him thirteen months before weren't.

...

January 5, 1968

When the plane touched American soil Eddie felt as if he was reborn. No longer, could he identify with the boy who wore a cap and gown to a high school graduation three years before. The boy, like Eddie's two friends, had become another casualty of the war. Unlike the other two, Eddie would never miss him.

140

Across the Footbridge

Becky couldn't stop the flow of tears that ran down her cheeks to make wet splotches on the back of Eddie's uniform. He was home! They had both survived.

The Christmas season that had passed without celebration returned to receive its due recognition.

It was December 11 when Becky removed the package from the mailbox. The same day Ginny received a letter and money order from Eddie. Becky's package contained the engagement ring that she now wore on her left hand and the matching wedding band that Eddie would place beside it in a few weeks.

The letter accompanying the money order instructed Ginny to use the money for the family's Christmas. Each time he looked into the eyes of a child in Vietnam he was reminded of the brothers and sister that he might never see again. He pleaded with his mother to do as he asked with the money. She had spent her last few cents to purchase and ship a package to him. He was with her in a shack in Kentucky and she was with him as he maneuvered through the jungle. She cashed the order that he sent and bought food for the others but she refused to make a Holiday feast with the possibility hanging over her that he might be dead.

...

Eddie and Becky left the airport and drove straight to his parents'. Ben had been watching for them for more than an hour when he saw the car. The pain of the past year was forgotten with their arrival and the joy in his family's faces was all that Becky saw when Eddie took her home to meet his parents. Ginny had scrubbed for days in preparation of

Across the Footbridge

Eddie's homecoming and Becky's first visit. The joy in her home that night would never be matched again.

Chapter Fourteen

Eddie would have to report to his base in two weeks but seven weeks after that he'd be home to stay. His first nights at home were filled with nightmares of the hell that he'd just escaped from. Ginny and Peggy attended Becky's bridal shower. After the party, Eddie made three trips between the house that hosted the party and Becky's parents, hauling all of their gifts. Ginny had never seen so many new things outside the big JC Penney store in town. Becky would never sew strips of muslin together and call them sheets.

A week before Eddie was to report to South Carolina he and Becky were married in her parents' living room. He asked Ben and Ginny to attend but they declined. They didn't have appropriate clothing and Ginny didn't want to embarrass him. Neither Ben nor Ginny realized that any humiliation he might have once felt for his parents and their living conditions had been lost in Vietnam. Unknowingly, they were rebuilding the wall that he had painstakingly dismantled.

Liphee and Michael were the only representation of Eddie's family at the small wedding. When, a few weeks later, Peggy saw pictures that were taken during and after the ceremony, she relived the same disappointment that she'd felt when she overheard her mother tell Eddie that she and his daddy wouldn't be there. Peggy wanted to be there but no one thought to extend her an invitation. She didn't have anything appropriate to wear either, but yearned for the opportunity to go to school and brag about a normal event that happened in normal families. With her disappointment held at bay, Peggy pored over the shots of Eddie kissing his bride as Becky's parents, brothers, sisters and Liphee looked on.

The day before he boarded the plane for South Carolina, Eddie signed the mortgage papers that entitled him and Becky to move into a small house one block from her parents. Eddie was buying a home.

While Ben and Ginny embraced Eddie's safe return they learned that another son would soon be leaving. Liphee announced to the family that she was relocating to a small town in Indiana where she and Ginny's cousin Ralph had moved a few years before. Larry was moving with her. He had come to realize that without an education he would never earn a descent living in his hometown. One month after Eddie and Becky moved into their new house, Liphee, George and Larry left Kentucky. Within two weeks all three had taken factory jobs and Liphee returned for Michael who had been left in Ginny's care.

Across the Footbridge

Maggie cried when Liphee's stationwagon pulled out of the driveway and she watched it out of sight, her view of the people inside blocked by the household items that were stuffed into the back. Liphee and George were living two states away and Mary was contemplating returning to her husband who dangled the possibility of their reconciliation in front of her. Fueled by the thought of regaining her oldest daughter, she returned to her marriage. Judy Ann remained with her aunt and three days later Mary returned to her mother's house. Three weeks later when she began running to the outhouse in the early morning hours, Maggie told her to count ahead eight months. That's when the baby would be due.

Eddie returned home the following month and was hired at the refinery just as he predicted two years before. He filled the little house with new furniture and six months later they told Ginny that her first grandchild would be born in the fall.

Liphee promised herself that she would return to her hometown fifty times in her first year in Indiana and fifty times she forced herself to stick it out for one more week. During those weeks Mary gave birth to twins and Becky presented Eddie with a son.

Ginny and Peggy were in the waiting room when the nurse came to tell them that Mary and both babies were doing fine. George returned a few days later to once again hold an infant in his arms. He sung every song known to him and a few unknown ones during three months of colic. By the time Mary's babies were sleeping through the night, Liphee was

145

Across the Footbridge

engaged. Three months later she returned to Kentucky with her new husband, John, and Michael to reopen her house and resume her job at the dry-cleaners.

Larry remained in Indiana till he turned eighteen. When he returned to his parents' home he brought a bride with him. He returned to his job at the dry-cleaners and two weeks later, when he received his first paycheck, he and Sally moved into an efficiency apartment in town. As if they'd never left, Liphee again pressed the shirts that he washed.

The day before Larry and Sally moved into their first home, Ginny divided everything in her kitchen into two piles, the larger of which she gave to Sally. Ginny spent several days sewing strips of muslin into sheets that she presented to Sally on the day that she and Larry moved out.

That winter, Liphee's husband, John, tried without success to find substantial employment that would support a family of three. The jobs that he did find were all minimum wage entry-level positions with no chance for advancement. In the spring he and Liphee closed up her house and returned to Indiana.

Ben located a house for rent closer to the little store where he spent his days. There was a well full of water a few feet from the kitchen door and again Ginny could be heard singing as she scrubbed the house and planted a garden. Every weekend, Eddie brought Becky and the baby to visit and Ben and Ginny relished in the knowledge that their grandson would never know the pain of hunger as their children had.

Larry and Sally were married for six months when she discovered that she was pregnant. That same week, Ben and

146

Across the Footbridge

Ginny made a trip to the state hospital in Lexington. There were several more appointments in the following weeks and the day after Eddie told them that Becky was expecting another baby Ginny was told that she had cancer.

She was alone when the doctor entered the examining room and placed the films of her throat on the lighted screen. He pointed to the gray mass and informed her that it was too large to remove. She would need six weeks of cobalt treatments to shrink the malignant tumor enough to allow him to remove it. He would have his nurse make the appropriate arrangements. Could she check back in a few hours?

Ben and Peggy had returned to the waiting room when an orderly came to escort Ginny to the x-ray room. The seats in the main lobby where they waited more than two hours were so soft that they lulled Peggy into a state of drowsy oblivion and she was startled by her mother's sudden appearance.

"Mommy, are you finished already? What did the doctor say?"

Ginny was clutching her elbows with opposite hands the way she did when she was upset.

"What did they say?"

Ben's words seemed to reach her and she nodded her head in the direction of the exit, then hurried towards the double doors with Ben and Peggy in pursuit. Once she was out of the hospital, she gave in to the trembling.

"I I I …have to come… bbbback. He ... says that I got cancer!"

Across the Footbridge

That moment of time became branded into Peggy's memory as the precise instant that her world began to change.

Two hours later they left the hospital to go home. Ginny would return in eight days to begin her treatments. Someone from Social Services had made arrangements for her room and board for the six weeks that she would receive cobalt. One of the large houses on the other side of the wide boulevard had been converted into dormitory rooms to accommodate the patients and families of University Hospital.

Larry received a promotion at the cleaners. The day that he began his training to operate the dry-cleaning machine Roger quit school and took the job of washing shirts. Another brother dropping out off school frightened Peggy. She loved school and the escape that it provided. The hours she spent in the classroom were the only spaces of time that she didn't have to think about not having enough money to buy food for the week or coal for the winter. Knowing that her education was her ticket out of the poverty, as it had been for Eddie, she wanted to even the odds of her mother's children. She wanted to be the second person in the family to complete high school.

The year before she'd been a freshman and no longer eligible for free books and lunches. Forty dollars, the cost of her books, was more than one third of the monthly disability check. Eight weeks before school resumed for the year their landlord asked Ginny if she and Peggy would be interested in doing laundry for the eight weeks that his wife would be recovering from surgery. Each Wednesday, Ginny and Peggy spent the morning in the basement of the landlord's home washing clothes on a wringer washer and hanging them to dry on a line in the back yard. In the afternoon they returned to take the clothes down and fold them. They earned five dollars a week, enough to cover the cost of Peggy's books.

Instead of starting her sophomore year Peggy went to Lexington with Ginny to start the radiation treatments. Eddie paid for a week's lodging for Peggy at the rooming house and provided money for her meals. That week Ginny learned her way around the large hospital and the cafeteria that provided her meals. On Friday evening they both returned home, Ginny for the weekend and Peggy to start school on Monday.

On Sunday, Ben delivered Ginny back to the rooming house and returned home alone. On Monday afternoon Peggy returned home from school to an empty house. She built a fire in the kitchen stove and carried in water, then did her homework and cooked supper. Ben and Roger still weren't home when dark came. When Ben did make it home both the food and the stove that it'd been cooked on were cold. With glassy eyes and the pungent odor of wine on his breath, Ben informed her that he wasn't hungry. By eight o'clock, he was passed out in his chair in front of the television. At ten o'clock Peggy turned off the television and went to bed. It was past midnight when she heard Roger's car. When she woke up the next morning she was alone again and the routine for the weeks that Ginny was in Lexington was set.

Every morning Ginny cautiously crossed the street in front of the medical center and entered through a side door of the building where she took the elevator to the basement and followed the main corridor to the x-ray department. The first day of her treatment, the technician drew black lines up and down and crossways on her throat to make a perimeter for the radiation. By the end of the first week the skin inside the black lines looked as if it had been roasting over hot coals. Each week the lines were redrawn, the area encased becoming smaller as the dosage of radiation was increased. At eight-thirty the treatment was over for the day.

The room where Ginny spent most of her time contained four metal beds and four small chests. One closet that ran the length of the room was divided into four spaces. Helen, who slept in the next bed and utilized the closet space on the right of Ginny, started her treatments a week before Ginny did. When Peggy and Ginny arrived, Helen replayed all the details of her surgery three weeks before while Peggy unpacked the two paper bags. She insisted on removing her blouse to display the patch of angry red skin that covered the area that was once her right breast, a scene that Peggy was reminded of each time she saw the effects of the cobalt on her mother's neck. The radiologist had explained the purpose of the radiation on the first treatment day. His intent was to destroy as many of the bad cells as he could, and would inevitably kill good cells in the process. Ginny's main concern was that she not lose her voice when the tumor was removed.

Her family's concern was that she live. Peggy faced the reality of her loss during the weeks that she came home to a cold empty house and realized that she'd taken for granted the life that her mother had put into their home. She missed the mother that had started the first fire of the day and managed to stretch little of nothing into a meal. The absence of her mother's voice couldn't be filled with the noise of the television that played on in the background. Counting the days till Ginny's return, Peggy bargained with a higher power. She would tolerate the poverty without complaint, just let her mother live.

One hundred and twenty miles away, Ginny was making bargains of her own. Each morning she followed her original route to and from the hospital. She passed the signs in the corridors and entrances that guided others to their destinations. To her, they were just scribbles and marks that she couldn't identify. She memorized where the button was on the panel in the elevator that when pushed would deliver her to the basement for her treatments and meals. The day that the elevator went straight to the sixth floor gave her a preliminary lesson on what her life would be like if she lost the ability to speak.

She entered the lift and pushed the button that was marked with a B. All of the other buttons were lit and instead of going down, she felt the elevator begin to climb. She began to panic when she heard the whine of the motor as it pushed her higher. Frantically, she began pushing buttons and eventually the lift slowed to a stop and after a brief pause the doors opened. The hallway in her line of vision was unfamiliar and after a few seconds the doors closed and she felt movement again. Each time the doors opened she stared into another strange hallway. After four stops the corridors all looked the same.

What she didn't know was that a bored eight-year-old had escaped the confines of his mother and nurses and rode the elevator to the ninth floor. Before leaving the lift he pushed all of the buttons in an attempt to distract his search party. On the fifth floor the doors opened and a nursing student entered the elevator and Ginny asked for directions to the cafeteria. The young girl pushed the button that delivered Ginny to the basement.

The technician positioned the light on the new lines and after assuring that the controls were set at the proper settings he asked Ginny if she was ready. She nodded and he left the room and appeared on the other side of the glass partition where he watched the blinking controls for twenty minutes. Ginny lay on the narrow table thinking about her experience in the elevator. That's what her life would be like if she couldn't talk.

...

"I can't read 'n write."

The surgeon looked across the width of his desk at the woman perched on the chair and then on to the shelves of books behind her. He'd been sitting in this same chair for twenty-eight years and had stopped counting the surgeries he performed more than ten years ago. After so many operations the patients had become lost in the procedures. He was an expert at what he did and no longer thought about the lives that he saved. He had surrendered that part of his career to the young interns that he trained. Suddenly, his perspective seemed to be a little off kilter. How long had he been like this?

He'd taken so much for granted for so very long. Oh, once, he remembered to say a prayer of thanks for his healthy legs after he removed a twenty-year-old's right leg just above

Across the Footbridge

the knee in an attempt to discourage the malignant cells that had invaded it. He encouraged the boy to get prosthesis as soon as possible. He would never run in a marathon but with pants on, in a few years, only his wife would know his secret.

Thousands of limbs he'd removed during the years and rarely had he thought to give thanks that all of his was still attached. The woman sitting in his office reminded him of a distant aunt that his grandmother once showed him a picture of, the same grandmother that exposed him to the power of the written word. According to Granny, you could become a prince or a pauper, a pirate or king. You could travel to any country or discover buried treasures in your own hometown, all by opening a book.

His top desk drawer was filled with the pamphlets that he doled out to his surgery patients, printed words that Ginny couldn't read. Without her voice she would be isolated with no possibility of learning another means of communication.

"Ginny, I understand what you are telling me. I will do everything in my power to leave you with as much of your voice box as possible. Okay?"

The weekend before the surgery Ben picked the beets in the garden and helped Ginny with the canning before she returned to the hospital. The morning that she was wheeled into the operating room she told Ben that she didn't want to survive if she couldn't speak. Eddie and Becky, Larry and Sally, Roger, Peggy, Liphee and Ben waited out the ten hours that the surgery lasted. Maggie waited at home with Mary and George.

Across the Footbridge

He'd worked all day to remove the tumor that had mated with her voice box. After five grueling hours one of the resident assistants questioned his procedure.

"Wouldn't it be much more efficient to remove the larynx along with the tumor. Wasn't he placing the patient at a higher risk of reoccurrence?"

"Doctor, how would you feel if I were performing surgery on your right hand and I decided to remove it instead of repairing it?"

"Doctor, I don't expect this woman's voice is as valuable to her as a hand is to a surgeon. My intention was to improve her prognosis."

"Apparently, you didn't do your case study as thoroughly as perhaps you should have. I assume that you will want to look over her chart again and then drop by my office afterwards to explain why we didn't make this one an easy in and out."

One by one, the other families had been summonsed when their loved one was taken to recovery. It was after six in the evening when the surgeon left the operating room.

"Hello folks, I'm Dr. Jacobs. I apologize for keeping you here all day. The surgery went fine and she's in recovery. It took a while to separate the tumor from her voice box, but I feel confident that I got all of the cancerous cells. She'll be in intensive care for the next forty-eight hours or so. You can peek in on her for a minute. She's tired. She fought hard today. She won't look too good to you tonight but the swelling will begin to recede in a few days and once it does she'll begin to get her voice back. She won't be able to raise the roof again but she will be able to express herself. If you don't have any questions, I'd like to get a cup of coffee and out of these scrubs."

The corridor in front of the intensive care unit was vacant. The only admissions this late would be emergency admissions. Ben and the rest of the family waited forty minutes while the nurses connected the tubes that would drain the fluids accumulating around the ten inch incision and hooked up the equipment that would monitor Ginny's vital signs and perform bodily functions for the next few days.

Two of the three nurses returned to the observation station and the third came to the door and called for Ben. They could go in two at a time for two minutes. After that they would need to observe the visitation rules.

Six remained in the hallway as two others walked through the swinging door. She was almost invisible under the sheets and miles of tubing. Her hair was the only identifiable feature as her face was swollen beyond recognition. The incision was exposed with several tubes draining fluid away from the area to disappear somewhere inside the machinery that they were attached too. Slowly her eyelids parted enough for her to see Peggy and Ben. Painfully, she raised the one hand that wasn't restrained to point to her mouth.

Ben interpreted her question.

"You can't talk now because of the tubes in your throat. The doctor said that you'll talk again as soon as they're out. He saved your voice box."

Chapter Fifteen

Liphee returned to Indiana the day after the surgery while Ginny remained in the hospital for ten days. The trips that Ben made to and from Lexington ate into his meager income and Peggy started her sophomore year without the required books. She sold her freshman books to the used bookstore at the high school and gave that money to her father to use for gas. Peggy borrowed books from friends with different class schedules and tried to do her homework in study hall and on her lunch break. Occasionally, someone would allow her to take a textbook home and on those evenings she tried to study ahead.

Across the Footbridge

Ginny was released from the hospital on a Friday. Peggy returned from school and built fires in both stoves before she cleaned the house in preparation for the homecoming. When dark came, she watched for her father's truck lights. Finally, Ben guided the old truck into the driveway and Peggy ran out to meet them.

After six weeks of radiation and two weeks of bed confinement, Ginny appeared much smaller and her voice was raspy but she could talk. Her first words after the surgery were barely audible whispers but Dr. Jacobs had been reassuring and just as he predicted her voice grew a little stronger each week. Ben and Peggy assisted her into the house and the bed that they'd moved into the front room.

On Monday, Peggy returned to school and Ben and Roger to their jobs. Before leaving for school Peggy put extra coal on the fire in the front room and set out food and water within Ginny's reach. She returned in the afternoon to find both the house and her mother chilled. Ginny didn't have enough strength to keep coal fed to the fire. On Tuesday and Wednesday Ben remained at home and kept the fires going. As soon as Peggy arrived in the afternoon, he left for the security of the little store and the wine that it supplied. Peggy cleaned the house or did the laundry and cooked super before she went to bed. The food that she put back for her father's dinner went untouched when he came home at bedtime with glassy eyes and slurred speech.

When Peggy got off the bus on Thursday Ben didn't hurry off as she had come to expect. After she changed out of her school clothes, he followed her out to the yard where she was taking in the wash from the evening before.

157

Across the Footbridge

"You can finish out the week, but...come Monday, you'll need to start staying home with your mother. I need to get back to my job."

He turned and walked away. She was eight months away from being legally old enough to do what he'd just told her that she must. She carried the armload of stiff cold clothes into the house and picked up the empty water bucket.

At school on Friday she informed her teachers that this would be her last day.

"We're moving into town this weekend so I'll have the school there contact you about having my records transferred."

She was quiet on the ride home. She'd cleaned out her locker and returned the borrowed books to their rightful owners before last period. She was almost to the bus after dismissal when she heard someone calling for her. Turning around, she saw one of her friends rushing across the parking lot. The parcel that the girl placed in Peggy's hand was wrapped in tissue paper and secured with red yarn.

"I'm sorry that I couldn't select your gift myself, but I did want you to have something to remember me by."

Debbie had called her mother that morning and pleaded with her to pick out something appropriate and deliver it to the school. The small wooden box was lined with purple velvet and the lid was etched in the pattern of roses. It would hold Peggy's dreams for the future that had been severed. Hugging the present to her chest, she knew that one part of her life was now over. She'd become a dropout at fifteen and her father could be put in jail for discontinuing her education. She swallowed back the guilt that she felt for deceiving her teachers and friends when she left the school bus for her last time.

The next morning Peggy began a new routine as a full-time homemaker to her mother, brother, and a father that was rarely home. Ben struggled in the beginning, not knowing what to say to Peggy, he began to avoid her. He hadn't wanted her to drop out of school but there just weren't any other options. Roger had purchased a car the month before and he had to keep his job in order to pay for that. The few days that Ben stayed home with Ginny were enough to show him that he needed his job, and the relief that it provided. The job supported his habit and he knew that the disability check wasn't enough to support it and the family too.

In an attempt to pacify Peggy, he began bringing her home treats from the store. It wasn't much but he wanted to show her that he appreciated her giving up her education to care for her mother. He always felt better if he had a candy bar or a bag of chips to offer her when he returned in the evenings.

Larry and Sally moved from the efficiency into a larger apartment at the other end of town. They were there a week when the apartment across the hall from them became available.

"I wonder if Grandma and Mary would be interested in it. George is leaving again next week and if they moved here then we would be close by if they needed anything."

After Sally cleaned up from the evening meal she and Larry went to visit Maggie and Mary.

The same day that George left for another season of picking fruit, Larry moved Maggie and Mary's dishes and personal items into Apartment 3D. In spite of the move, Maggie fretted most of the day.

"He just takes off without a thought to where he'll end up next. I told him that he'd probably be dead for six months before the news caught up to me!"

George had laughed at the sorrow-filled picture that she continued to paint.

"Don't you worry, Mommy. I promise that no matter where I'm at, when its time, I'll come home to die."

Ginny was slow in regaining her strength after the surgery and radiation. Neither she nor Peggy ever mentioned the fact that Peggy no longer attended school. Peggy kept herself going with the promise that she would return the next year. She wouldn't graduate with her original class but at least she would get her diploma. She always made sure that she was inside when it was time for the school bus to pass the house. She didn't need one of her former classmates reporting that she hadn't moved but was actually skipping school.

By the end of November it became impossible to keep the house warm with two stoves. Layers of ice began forming in the water bucket in the kitchen during the warmest part of the day. At Ginny's six-week post-op examination, Dr. Jacobs told her that if she wanted to have a complete recovery she would need to be kept warm and eat a proper diet. When a larger apartment became available in the building where Maggie and Larry lived, Maggie and Mary moved there and Roger signed a three-month lease on the one that they vacated and moved there with Peggy and Ginny for the three months that his mother needed to recuperate. Ben elected to stay behind.

Across the Footbridge

"I'm gone most of the time anyway. I'll drive in and visit on my days off."

Once again circumstances had brought Maggie and Ginny under the same roof.

Roger went to work each morning and returned to the apartment afterwards. After paying rent, making his car payment and buying gas for his car, he had fifteen dollars left each week of which he gave Peggy twelve-fifty to wash their clothes at the coin-op and buy food for three, shelving his own social life for the months that they were in the apartment. Peggy managed to feed Ginny three balanced meals each day and provide lunches for Roger to take to work, her budget so tight that she bought the same items each week and prepared the same meals weekly. Ben drove into town once a week to visit his wife but never stayed to take a meal.

Mary was first to notice that Ginny was beginning to withdraw. During her first weeks in the apartment, she stayed with Mary and Maggie if Peggy went to the grocery or to the laundry. She usually napped till Peggy returned, her body still recovering from the effects of the cancer. The only activity that she engaged in was her own personal care. Peggy still prepared all of the meals and put them on the table before she called her mother to come eat.

Peggy enjoyed caring for the small apartment with the aid of running water and inside plumbing. She began to relax once she was removed from the pressure of hiding from the bus and school officials. Sometimes, she pretended that the furniture and floors that she scrubbed were hers and an imaginary husband would enjoy the food that she prepared. Maybe, if she hadn't been so involved in her make-believe world she would have taken notice of what was happening around her.

They had come to accept Ginny's quiet demeanor as a result of the surgery and recovery. Gradually, she began to refuse to be left alone and Mary noticed that she was interacting with the family less, but assumed that it was because she was homesick for Ben. The weeks slipped away and Ginny's strength returned but she made no attempt to resume any of her previous activities.

One weekend Liphee returned for a visit. She was pleased with the healing of the incision but noticed that Ginny talked less than was normal but contributed it to the fact that her voice was now hoarse. In an attempt to reassure herself, she asked Ginny about her mood before she left.

"I just miss Ben."

Four weeks later, Roger released the apartment and returned to the house with his mother and sister. Larry and Sally moved to another apartment closer to the dry-cleaners while Mary and Maggie moved back to the house across from Liphee's.

Ben was pleased when his family returned. The long winter months had reminded him of the times that he and Ginny had separated when the kids were small. The day that they were to come home he carried in coal and drawed two pails of water before he went to work at the store.

Peggy utilized the water and many more buckets as she scrubbed away three month's worth of bachelor dirt. Ginny continued her days as if she was still in the apartment, never commenting on the results of Peggy's labor or even acknowledging the need for it.

Across the Footbridge

On a cold February morning Larry and Peggy sat in the waiting room of the local hospital, both trying to follow the plot of a bad movie that was playing on the small screen mounted into the ceiling.

"Mr. Rice?"

He had hair the color of carrot juice and a redder face. His eyelids were scrunched together as if he would rather be asleep and when his fist came into contact with his open mouth, he immediately began to nuzzle. He was beautiful.

Larry stood there for a long time as the nurse on the other side of the glass wall turned the baby this way and that so his father could count fingers and toes. He had a son. Within three weeks he knew that he couldn't stay. His wages just wouldn't stretch far enough to cover the expenses of an infant. Promising himself that his would never know the pain of hunger, he and Sally made plans to return to Indiana.

"Can we stay here till we save enough money to move back to Indiana?"

...

Ginny spent her days in the rocking chair just holding him and watching him sleep. Everyday Ben commented on how much he resembled Larry when he was a baby, something that she couldn't recall. Every morning she went to the room where Larry and Sally slept and plucked him out of the bassinet. She rocked him through the day and mentally sung the tunes that her voice would no longer carry, only relinquishing him to his mother for a bath or diaper change.

The car was already packed when Larry removed him from his grandmother's arms.

Across the Footbridge

In late April Becky delivered another son. Ginny's response to the birth of this grandson was less than it had been for the first two. Through that spring Peggy continued to keep the house and do the cooking and washing. Ginny moved from the front room to the front porch, as the days grew warmer. She showed no interest in the upkeep of her home or the planting of a garden. Ben dug up a small area and planted a few tomato plants.

Roger met a girl in town and began spending all of his evenings with her. When the days became longer Ben stayed at the store later. A few times he came home in time for supper but on those occasions he returned as soon as he finished eating. Before, the evening meal had been the time that he and Ginny discussed everything from politics and religion to the names of deceased relatives. Now, she took her meal in silence and he rarely ate.

The first week in June Peggy's birthday came and went without any recognition. She was old enough to date and could officially quit school. These were her birthday presents she told herself as she carried a bucket of bleach water to the outhouse. She pretended that she was Cinderella when she scrubbed the seat and floor of the primitive toilet. Some days she would have welcomed a wicked stepmother and ugly stepsisters, or anyone that she could have a normal conversation with. Reality told her that her prince wasn't going to knock at the front door with a lost shoe in his hand.

"And I thought she had it rough!"

Peggy chuckled when she realized that she was actually talking to herself.

Across the Footbridge

It was after nine when Ben's boss drove past the store and turned around and came back.

"Ben, you should've locked up hours ago. It's Friday night and anyone drinking tonight will be across the bridge by now."

He'd sat behind the counter for more than two hours in hopes that a customer would happen by to justify his staying open late. That would've eased his guilty conscience about not going home. He'd approached Ginny again the night before. It'd been eight months since the surgery and she should be feeling better by now. He'd even asked Dr. Jacobs about it the week before when he told Ginny that she wouldn't need to come back for three months.

"Doc, when can she start doing things again?"

Jacobs turned to Ben. It wasn't fair that some people had more luck than they deserved and others like Ben and Ginny had none. The poverty that they were living in was burden enough but to throw the load of having cancer onto their weighted down shoulders was more than he liked to think about. At her last checkup Ginny had told him that her father had died from cancer.

"Well, if you die from cancer, it won't be this one. Everything is looking good and your voice is stronger than I would have dared to hope for. Of course, we're going to keep a close eye on you, but I think that we've got his one whipped."

Jacobs became concerned with Ben's question. Ginny's incision had healed nicely and her voice was strong enough to be heard from a room away. She should have resumed normal activities months ago.

165

Across the Footbridge

"Mr. Rice, she can resume all of her normal activities. In fact I recommend that she do just that. I want to see her in three months to check for any buildup of scar tissue. As we discussed before, we have to wait five years before we call it a cure, but I think we'll be able to do just that."

Ben returned to the present and followed the owner out to his car.

"Ben, I hope you understand why I can't pay you for the extra hours that you've been putting in around here. If more customers were coming in then I'd have the extra income to support your additional hours, but they aren't and I don't. You can go back to closing at five again if you want."

The sun had already dropped behind the hills when Ben turned into the driveway. Oh God! How he dreaded going inside. Ever since they'd made the trip to the hospital the week before, he'd been encouraging Ginny to start doing things again but she seemed to look past him or through him when he tried to make eye contact with her. And... she hadn't been paying much attention to the grandkids when they came out.

He sat in the darkness finally allowing the thoughts that he'd been pushing back for weeks to surface. Fear rose in him with a sobering effect as memories of the past moved before his closed eyes. It couldn't be that; she only got that way after the kids were born. Except for the time that he saw her and Pappy at that office in town. That time she hadn't had a baby. He was sure of that because he was the first man she'd ever been with. He pushed against the door handle and stepped out of the truck. Reaching behind the seat he withdrew a fifth of Musketel and, with one long swallow,

166

drank half of it. He replaced the lid and shoved the bottle back into its hiding place before he shut the truck door and headed for the outhouse. It wouldn't happen again. It couldn't happen again.

It was after midnight when Roger parked his car beside his dad's truck. He would have to get up in less than five hours. He made a trip to the outhouse before he went inside.

Peggy built a fire in the kitchen stove to heat water to wash the dishes left overnight from supper. She washed the dishes and filled three lines with laundry before eleven. Lately, the afternoons seemed to drag by as she tried to fill her hours. She watched three soap operas while she waited for the clothes to dry and after they were folded and put away, she went to the well to draw water for supper. Three times that afternoon, she asked Ginny the same question without getting a response.

"Mommy, I asked you if I can go to Grandma's tomorrow when Roger goes to work!"

"Daddy, I'm going to town tomorrow when Roger goes to work."

"Is your mother goin' with you?"

"I tried to ask her three times today."

Peggy was in Roger's car when it left the driveway at six-thirty the next morning.

She'd been spending too much time alone and having conversations with herself just for an opportunity to talk. This is what she told Mary later that day. Her grandmother asked about her mother and why she didn't come in with her.

"I hope that she ain't gittin' sick again."

167

Across the Footbridge

"Grandma, what do you mean? Are you talking about Mommy's cancer coming back?"

Maggie never answered.

The house, where she and Mary lived with Mary's three children, consisted of three small rooms. Its location had become known as The Bottom, due to the geographical fact that it was the only level ground in the area. An elderly widow owned the house that Maggie rented, three others that she rented to members of her family and the house that she lived in and one in front of Maggie's. When the larger house in front became available, Peggy and Roger helped Mary carry the furniture and kids across the yard. Peggy had been going into town with Roger one day a week to break up the monotony of the long summer days.

July 3, 1970,

After an absence of more than six months, George returned home. His face was brown from the months he'd spent picking fruit in Florida sunshine.

July 8, 1970,

Peggy filled the lines with laundry, then filled a bucket with the water that she used to rinse the clothes. She poured Clorox in the bucket and carried it and an old broom to the outhouse. She scrubbed the floor and seat of the toilet, then went to the kitchen and made her mother a sandwich for lunch. It was after eleven and Ginny was still in bed. Peggy went to the doorway of her parents' bedroom.

"Mommy, are you ready for lunch? I left a sandwich on the table for you. I'm going to the backyard for a while."

Across the Footbridge

Peggy had started spending her afternoons lying on a blanket in the sun. Closing her eyes, she could drift to another world where everything was as it was intended to be. Some days she returned to the county high school as a gifted student and earned the scholarships that she dreamed of a few years before. Other times she was a pretty cheerleader dating the star quarterback. When the sun dropped behind the big tree at the side of the house she knew that it was time to put away her pretend life and go inside to start supper.

Peggy changed into her swimsuit then picked up a blanket and a magazine that Mary gave her earlier in the week. Ginny was sitting at the table when she went through the kitchen and out the door.

"Mommy, just leave your plate and I'll wash it when I come in. I'll need to heat water for my bath anyway."

Chapter Sixteen

The sun's heat accumulated through the morning hours, rising from the pavement it drifted through the opened door, then circulated till it filled every room with its muggy presence. George had been home a week when he began to get restless. He heard that a place out on the highway was hiring so he went there instead of the bus station as he usually did. He returned a little before noon to find Mary filling the lines in the back yard with small clothes. She picked up the empty basket and followed him into the house.

"Mary, Mommy said that she thought that Ginny might be getting' sick again. She don't mean that kind of sick, does she?"

Across the Footbridge

"I hope not. She's been quiet since she had her throat operated on. Maybe that's all it is. I was little when she got that way before but I sure remember what she was like after Peggy was born. Mommy's been worrying about her for a month or more. The last time she came in with Ben she didn't say four words the whole time that they were here."

"I talked to that man about the job this mornin'. He said that I could have it but I'd have to leave for northern Ohio tomorrow mornin'. Maybe, I should plan on stickin' around here for a while."

"I think I'd feel better if you did."

Mary had long since given up on reclaiming her oldest child. Judy Ann was almost eight years old and didn't even remember the eighteen months that she'd been Mary's daughter. She called her aunt and uncle Mommy and Daddy and Mary wouldn't take her away from her home and bring her to the day to day existence that was all that she could offer. The support checks and Maggie's social security check barely stretched from month to month.

Larry and Sally had been living in Indiana four months. He found a job that paid more than twice what he'd earned in Kentucky. There was opportunity for advancement at the plant and he was thinking about trying to get his G.E.D. His boss told him that he would need that in order to get a promotion. His son had grown into a fat content baby with hair that was still bright orange and his eyes had turned blue like Sally's.

Becky's youngest was three months old and her older boy had gone from walking to running since the baby was born. Some days she wondered about her own sanity. Two in diapers kept her in the utility room or running to the back yard with another basket of wet diapers under her arm. And, some people wondered how she had lost her weight so fast after the baby was born.

Roger had taken the job that Larry left when he went back to Indiana. For the first time he had a few extra dollars in his pocket. He'd bought some nicer clothes and a nicer car. The car was really something. That was what his girlfriend kept telling him. A red Dodge Dart convertible, the day that he drove it off the lot he felt like the whole county was staring at him.

Ben carried the last of the boxes to the pit at the back of the store lot, keeping his ear tuned in the direction of the front door. The bell that he'd tied on the doorknob sometimes moved with the breeze. Several times he'd made a hasty exit from the outhouse to find the store empty. There wasn't enough wind today to ruffle the wings of a mosquito. That was why he decided to burn the excess boxes accumulating in the back room.

At the house, Peggy drifted off to sleep after an hour or so. She knew that it was a little after twelve cause she'd went to the toilet earlier and went through the kitchen to check on her mother. She noticed the time when she looked in on her mother who was lying in bed again with her back turned towards the doorway. Peggy tiptoed past the bed and on through the front door. She walked around the front of the house and fell back on the blanket. Stretching out again, she placed the opened magazine on her face and soon was asleep.

When she woke sometime later, she was dizzy from the heat. Sitting upright she tried to bring her blurry vision

172

into focus. The sun had moved enough that the tree in the side yard shaded more than half of her legs. Trying to bend her knees she realized that she should have turned over sooner. Slowly, she rose from the blanket and moved towards the kitchen door.

The kitchen was dark and cool and she drank two glasses of water before she looked at the clock. It was two-forty. She went to the next room to see if Ginny was still asleep. The bed was empty. She went to the front porch to see if she was sitting out there. She wasn't. She checked the outhouse and the other side of the yard.

"Mommy!"

The silence grew as the clock on the kitchen wall ticked off individual seconds. Peggy went through the four rooms again, then the outhouse and yard.

"Mommy!"

She was gone. This time Peggy looked inside the hole in the toilet and under the beds. The clothes that she'd hung that morning had dried into stiff mocking forms. Ginny's lunch plate was still on the table where Peggy placed. A glob of mustard and a piece of the crust from the bread were all that remained.

"Mommy! Where are you?"

Peggy passed the clock in the kitchen again, three-twenty. She pulled a pair of shorts and a shirt over her swimsuit, then went to look up and down the road in front of the house. All she saw was a dog sniffing at a dead squirrel about fifty yards away.

"M-o-mmmeee!"

Across the Footbridge

She went to search the high weeds at the back of the house that started behind the well and grew to meet the trees in the distance. She returned to the house fifteen minutes later with briar scratches marring the skin on her thighs and green burrs attached to the legs of her shorts. She walked through the silent house again before she went back to the road. She could hear the tractor's engine before she could see it. Watching from the edge of the driveway the tractor finally emerged at the top of the hill and slowly made its way towards her. The driver and tractor grew in size as they approached and the rumble grew loud enough to drown out the sound of Peggy's racing heart.

Waving both arms at him she flagged down the farmer that lived two miles west. When he was directly in front of her he killed the engine and removed his hat.

"Have you seen a woman about forty years old with black hair? She was wearing a floral print house dress."

He swatted at a fly that was hovering around his face with his hat, then turned in the seat to stare in the direction that he'd just come from. Settling his hat back in place his answer was lost in the rumble of the tractor as it came to life.

"Haven't seen anybody wearin' a dress that color today!"

It was four-eighteen the last time Peggy searched the kitchen. She had to tell her father. Without a phone at the store she would have to walk there to tell him. She'd just reached the road when she spotted a truck coming towards her. From where she was it looked like her father's. When the truck slowed in front of the house she saw her mother in the

Across the Footbridge

passenger seat. Relief flooded through her as she realized all of the needless panic that she'd just put herself through.

"Wait till I tell Daddy what all I thought had happened!"

She was still smiling when Ben cut the motor. He opened his door and got out without looking at Peggy. He went to the other side and opened the door where Ginny was sitting.

"Daddy, when did you come and get Mommy?" You won't believe the things that went through my head when I couldn't find her."

Ben reached inside the truck and grabbed Ginny's feet and pulled them around till she faced him. Leaving her feet to dangle over the edge of the seat, he grabbed her hands then pulled her to her feet. Peggy stood looking on as her father led her mother past her and into the house. She was wearing faded canvas tennis shoes and the white cotton underslip that she wore for pajamas in the summer. Peggy would never find the dress that her mother had been wearing when she went outside.

Inside the house, Ben led his wife through the front room to the iron bed that they had shared for years. He pushed her to a sitting position on the edge of the bed and removed her shoes before he pushed her head towards the pillow. He lifted her legs onto the bed and covered them with a blanket. Peggy watched from the doorway as he straightened the shoes then turned to face her. He looked into her eyes briefly then nodded towards the kitchen. Peggy followed.

175

Across the Footbridge

His face was flushed and a muscle in his right cheek twitched with an occasional contraction. He looked over her and past her but not at her when he spoke.

"Peggy Ann, you can't let your mother out of your sight, ever again."

She heard his footsteps take him back through the house, then the slam of his truck door. She waited for the sound of the truck's engine but all she heard was the methodical ticking of a clock.

Chapter Seventeen

August 6, 1970

"I'll be home a little after ten."

She turned right at the side of Maggie's house and five minutes later opened the door to the cool darkness of the little store. She'd been operating the register behind the counter for two weeks. The girl she was relieving, closed the magazine she was reading and placed it on a shelf under the counter. Peggy passed her at the end of the meat counter.

"See ya tomorrow."

Across the Footbridge

She opened the drawer of the register and pulled from underneath the tray the slips of paper kept there. Locating the one with her name on it, she wrote fifteen-cents at the bottom and returned it to the drawer then walked across the room to the pop cooler.

A door opened off the back wall leading into the owner's living quarters behind. The wall behind the cash register separated the store from the poolroom on the other side. An open window in the middle of the wall provided access to the person behind the register. During the evening hours, quarters, dimes and nickels could be seen on the ledge of the window opening.

The commercial area was divided into two rooms. The front room contained the grocery items that lined the walls and metal shelves that divided the floor into small aisles. The back room contained two pool tables, three pinball machines and a jukebox.

The pool tables in back had become a community-gathering place through the years where for a nickel a game, the boys and men in the area had a place to come to that removed them from the wife and kids or a mother who wanted her son behind a lawnmower. This was where Roger met the girl who monopolized most of his evening hours and where Eddie came a couple of times a week to shoot pool with some of the guys he went to school with. George came here to purchase the gallons of milk Mary continued to pour into baby bottles.

More than an hour passed after Peggy entered the store before the first customer of her shift walked through the door. The clang of the bell brought her back from thoughts of the past seven weeks.

Across the Footbridge

Four weeks before:

Peggy stood in the kitchen for almost an hour trying to absorb the events of the afternoon, waiting for the sound of her father's truck or his steps leading him back into the house. At five-forty, she walked past her mother's bed and through the front room to the porch. Ben was sitting in the front of the truck with his head resting on the steering wheel. Peggy walked to the clothesline and removed the clothes she'd hung there earlier in the day. Her father was still in the same position when she passed the truck again, her arms filled with clean laundry. The three weeks that followed, was a horrible nightmare that refused to release Ginny or her family from its tenacious grasp.

Ben sat in the truck that day till darkness came and separated him from the house where his wife lay staring at some invisible object in front of her. When he entered the dark house, Peggy was in bed. She'd folded the laundry before building a fire in the stove to heat water for the dishes and her bath. She bathed in the kitchen and instead of hanging a quilt over the doorway leading into her parents' bedroom as she usually did, she placed it between the bedroom and front room. Ginny's body remained rigid and silent while her daughter bathed at the sink in the next room. Peggy placed her swimsuit, shorts, and shirt in the tub of the wringer washer at the corner of the kitchen and carried the pan of used water to the back door where she gave it a sling into the darkness. The heat from the stove drifted through the open doorway to mix with the coolness of the night.

She closed the kitchen door and went to the room off

the front room that contained her bed. She heard her father come in and close the front door sometime later. She was awake for a long time, the sound of her father's sleeping was the last thing that she heard before sleep removed her from the day that was still replaying in her head. When she opened her eyes, daylight was sifting through the window of the bedroom and Ben was standing in the doorway.

"You'd better git up and keep an eye on your mother. I'll be leaving for work in a little bit."

For five days, Peggy tried to monitor her mother at all times. She returned every minute or so from the clotheslines, to see her mother sitting in a chair or her still form lying on a bed. The third day, she started utilizing the windows during the times she needed to be in the yard. On the morning of the sixth day, Roger's car stopped in front of a house at the edge of town and in the gray light of the early morning dawn, Peggy led her mother through the door of her grandmother's house.

"I'll be back to pick you up when I get off work."

There had been small spaces of time during the last five days when Peggy thought that maybe she dreamed the whole thing, times when her mother appeared as she had the week before, quiet but alert. Occasionally she responded if Peggy asked her a question and a few times even initiated a conversation. Then almost as soon as it began it was over and Ginny would withdraw into the inner sanctuary that hid her from Peggy's view. Five days of fear and mental turmoil had taken its toll on the frightened sixteen-year-old who led her mother through her grandmother's door.

She hadn't seen her father sober since the nightmare began. The few times that they had made eye contact, she saw

Across the Footbridge
the tears he struggled to hold back and his eyes held the same
pain that she saw in her own.

"Why didn't someone take her to a doctor?"

For more than two hours Maggie and Mary talked
about the years following Peggy's birth, and other times before
she was born. Ginny was lying on her mother's bed two
rooms away, unaware of Peggy's introduction to the nightmare
that'd been a part of her life for more than twenty-five years.
"We did take her to a doctor. When it happened the
first time, your grandpa took her to every doctor within fifty
miles. They told him to take her home and take care of her,
that she should come out of it. They told us we could place
her in the state hospital, but that she'd probably die there.
One doctor said there were too many patients there for them
to keep an eye on em' all the time."
Peggy yearned to wake from the nightmare and find her
mother in the garden in the back yard with a bucket of green
beans that she'd picked.
"How long will she be like this?"
"I don't know...one time it took her more'n two years.
That was after you were born. We thought that if she didn't
have any more babies, she'd be all right."
"That's why Pappy didn't want her and your daddy to
get married."
"I thought you said that she only got this way after she
had us kids!"
"She did, except for that one time before she met and
married your daddy. She was about seventeen then...wasn't
181

she George?"

Hearing the horror tales of her parents' lives, Peggy thought that it couldn't have been real. Nobody could survive the years that her uncle and grandmother described to her.

Peggy continually returned with her mother to her grandmother's house each day that Roger went to work. On the fourth afternoon, she walked to the store two blocks away to purchase a gallon of milk, and, while she was there, was offered the job behind the counter. She accepted.

Ben and Roger were upset about it with her father accusing her of deserting her family.

"Daddy, I'm not deserting anyone and there's a house for rent behind Grandma and Mary that we can move into. I can't take care of Mommy by myself! I told you that I would use the money I make to buy groceries so you'll still have money to pay for your wine."

The following week Ben gave up his job and Peggy started hers. She worked six-hour shifts at the store, six days a week. Her schedule was either ten to four during the day or four to ten in the evenings. The house they moved to consisted of three small rooms with the kitchen barely big enough to hold the refrigerator, stove and table. As they had done years before, the table was pushed against a wall to allow enough room to walk between it and the stove. The two beds, dresser, and chest took up most of the space in the room that connected the kitchen and the front room. The front room had a small gas burner that replaced the iron coal stove and a door in the kitchen opened onto a small back porch that held the old wringer washer. Another door in the front room led to a small porch at the front of the house. Fifteen feet in front of this

Across the Footbridge

porch was where Ben's yard ended and Maggie's began.

After hearing the horrible stories of her mother's illness, Peggy realized that the nightmare she couldn't wake from would probably last for a long time. Ben still drank every day and on the days that she worked the first shift at the store, he would be waiting by the door for her to return home. He left as soon as she appeared and about an hour later she would hear the truck tires crunching the gravel of the driveway that ran past the kitchen door. He made daily trips across the river and if Peggy worked the evening shift, he took his drive in the morning hours.

Ben watched over Ginny as Liphee had done years before, walking her to the outhouse then waiting outside until she opened the door to signal that she was ready to leave. Some days, he took her there and helped her with her clothing as Liphee had years before. The family surrounded Ginny watching her day and night. There were no more conversations about the illness. Eddie helped his brother and father move the furniture into the house and assemble the beds before he returned to his own home.

Maggie now suffered from the same fear that her husband carried with him till the day he died. She lay awake through the long nights, thinking of the conversations they'd had in the nights of long ago. She still missed him and several times in the last few weeks had raised her right hand to place it over his heart, only to have it fall to the flat covers at her side.

"Charley, I'm afraid without you here to help watch over her."

George sometimes overheard the whispered conversations Maggie had with her dead husband and he too, wished that his father was there to help protect his sister.

Peggy saw Eddie two or three times a week when he came to the store to purchase a gallon of milk or shoot a game of pool but the conversations between them never touched on their mother's illness, or the reason that she was now working and their father wasn't.

It was Labor Day weekend and Larry and Sally returned to Kentucky to visit his family. The baby Larry held in his arms held no resemblance to the infant that Ginny had held on her lap months before. When Larry placed his son in his mother's arms that Saturday afternoon Ginny responded as she would have if the laughing baby had been a bag of rocks someone asked her to hold. Larry left abruptly a few minutes later, his heart filled with the pain of his mother's open rejection of him and his son. Peggy stood watching as the pride in her brother's eyes was replaced with first pain and then anger. He lifted his son from his grandmother's lap and walked out the door. Peggy felt his pain and her own for not running after him and telling him the truth.

Liphee and Michael returned to Maggie's the same weekend. As soon as Liphee looked into Ginny's eyes, she knew that the monster from the past had returned again to lay claim to her sister. Peggy led her mother out of Maggie's door and down the path in the grass that was becoming more recognizable. Liphee watched them disappear through the opening in the hedge that grew between the two houses, then turned to face her brother.

"How long has she been like this?"

"Peggy brought her here one morning about two months ago. She said she'd fell asleep in the yard earlier that week and when she woke up, Ginny was gone. Ben brought her home about two hours later."

On Monday morning, Liphee steered her car across the bridge that connected her to the interstate highway that'd take her home. Her thoughts traveled back through the years as her car traveled north.

On Tuesday, the local schools opened their doors for the new school year and Peggy washed the kitchen floor instead of resuming her education. She knew now that she'd never pick up the life she'd set aside a year before.

The leaves on the trees turned from green to shades of amber and orange before turning brown to fall in front of Peggy's feet as she walked to work and back. Each week, the owner of the store removed the papers at the bottom of the register and tallied up the numbers and subtracted the purchases from the amount that he owed his employees. Three out of four weeks, Peggy owed more than she earned. The first week of every month Ben paid the balance when his disability check arrived and Peggy had one week's earnings to spend as she wished. Once a month she rode the bus into town and spent whatever money she had on clothes.

Her hours behind the counter at the store were the only hours she had to be a teenager as she sat on the stool and watched the pool games in process behind the back wall. The owner told her the first day that she could feed some of the nickels placed on the window ledge into the jukebox in the corner. Peggy came to recognize who held the cue sticks behind the wall by the songs that filtered through the open doorway and window. For six hours, six days a week she was just a girl behind a cash register. She learned the names of the regular customers and the men who drove the milk and bread trucks and the local high school boys that stopped on their way home from school each day. As soon as her shift was over, she walked home to relieve her father of her mother's care.

The treetops were bare limbs that hardly stirred as the cold November wind moved through them. Peggy rushed inside and hurriedly closed the door behind her. The front room was empty and she heard nothing but the sound of the old refrigerator's motor coming from the kitchen. She walked through the other two rooms and out the kitchen door and followed the path around the house and through the yard that separated her from her grandmother's door. Most afternoons, Ben led Ginny across the yard to his mother-in-laws, where he watched the soaps that had come to fill some of the hours of the long fall days.

Peggy found her mother and father sitting side by side on her grandmother's couch. Her aunt and uncle were sitting in chairs in the front room and Maggie's form was visible on the bed in the next room. The TV screen was dark and silent and immediately Peggy sensed the tension when she pulled the door closed behind her.

Ginny had been missing for more than two hours that day. Ben left her to go to the outhouse about one o'clock and intended to return for her before he went to the house next door. No one saw her leave. Each neighbor's door that he and Mary knocked on netted the same results. At three-fifteen, Ben saw her coming through the opening in the hedge that separated the two yards, shivering from more than two hours of exposure to the cold temperature. She hadn't spoken since.

Across the Footbridge

...

Larry and Sally moved into a mobile home that they'd purchased the month before. Behind the trailer the yard met the edge of a creek that reminded him of the creek of his childhood. He pushed his empty supper plate towards the middle of the table, turning to the baby seated on his right. His son was nine months old and the constant banging of a spoon against the metal tray on the highchair was starting to annoy both of his parents.

"And we think we want to add more racket to our meals?"

The question he directed towards Sally didn't require a response.

"Are you sure you don't wanna' go see your mom for Thanksgiving?"

"I never said that I don't wanna go see her. I said that I don't think she would care one way or another. You'd think after a while I'd learn!"

"So, you want to stay home for Thanksgiving?"

"Yea, I want to stay home where I know that I'm wanted!"

Larry fought back angry tears for most of the seven-hour drive that took him home on Labor Day. He knew that Eddie didn't receive the kind of treatment that he did when he took his sons to his mother's house.

He didn't know that Eddie had almost stopped taking Becky and the boys to visit his parents. He tried to push what was happening to the back of his mind, the same area where he stored his memories from Nam. He wanted to tell

187

Across the Footbridge

Becky where he'd been the day that his dad called him to come and help search for his mother but he didn't know how to share it with her. It wasn't that he thought that she wouldn't understand. He didn't understand it himself. He still remembered things from his childhood that he tried to forget and now those memories were rushing up through the years, and he felt the same fear that he'd felt as a child. He was wrapping that fear in a blanket of anger that he had no direction for. The few times that he'd taken Becky and the boys out there, they'd only stayed a few minutes and then left. He recognized the distant look in his mother's eyes, the same one that separated him from her when he was young. As he shut out the fear of what was happening inside his mother, he also shut out his wife and children. Becky struggled to understand what was coming between her and the husband who lay in silence on his side of the bed.

The monster had returned with all of the power of its previous attacks, removing Ginny from her family and leaving a wide path of destruction in its wake.

...

After Mary filled Peggy in on the events of the afternoon, she went to the bed where Maggie lay facing the wall.

"Mommy are you all right?"

She'd gone to the bed right after Ben asked George and Mary if they would help look for her. She spent the next two hours in silent prayer while fear of her daughter's future became a weight of heavy dread that seemed to seep into the center of her heart and from there spread little by little into every limb of her body.

Across the Footbridge

"Mary, I know that your Daddy was right all those years ago an' I don't know how I'll go on when something happens to her."

...

"Daddy, we have to do something!"

Ginny was silent on the ride to the hospital. Hours later, on the ride home, Peggy's eyes continued to return to the empty space between her and Ben.

Ginny was placed behind the locked doors that separated that wing of the hospital from the rest of the building. Forty-eight hours passed. Two days in which Peggy was relieved from the burden of responsibility that she'd carried for more than four months. It was enough time for a seed of hope for the future to start to take root. The doctors would know what was happening, and they would know how to fix it.

Peggy's relief was short lived and the optimism that had just begun to take root, withered and died three days later. After forty-eight hours of observation, Ginny was released to her family. The X-rays showed nothing that would indicate a tumor and Ginny had remained in the same catatonic state for the duration of her hospital stay. Her family could take her home and care for her...or...they could place her in an institution.

The day after she returned from the hospital, Ginny quietly walked out the front door while Ben was in the kitchen making coffee.

Peggy was straightening the rows of candy bars in the glass display case under the front counter when she heard the clang of the bell. She rose from her knees and turned towards the front of the counter. She saw the raw fear in her uncle's face.

"Your Mom's gone again! Ben said that you'd better come home and help us look for her."

...

The Friday before Thanksgiving, Peggy returned home from work to find Ben on the front porch. He was tightening a bolt on the lock that he'd just installed on the outside of the door. He'd become the warden in the three-room prison where his wife was confined.

Peggy recognized the look on Roger's face an hour later when he saw the new locks that his father had installed on both doors---locks that shut his mother in, instead of shutting the world out. Peggy sat on the side of the bed she now shared with Ginny and watched while Roger shaved over the kitchen sink. He was eighteen and she was sixteen. Neither of them knew how to express the mutual fear that had become a part of the same bonding that connected them to their parents.

"Do you want to go anywhere tonight? If you do I'll stay home."

How had they both grown into adults without passing through adolescence? Her brother's head almost touched the bare light bulb dangling from the ceiling.

"That's okay. If I go over to watch TV with Mary, I'll take her with me."

"Does this look okay?"

The sweater he pulled over his head was one she hadn't

Across the Footbridge

seen before.

"It looks great, but what's the special occasion? You planning on proposing to her tonight?"

"Nah...I'm not seeing her anymore."

Peggy was smiling at the prospect of Roger dumping his first girlfriend when she heard his car leave the driveway and turn in the opposite direction of the way he usually went.

Ginny huddled on the end of the couch and Ben was passed out in the chair across from her. A few minutes later, Peggy placed her mother's arms in her coat and led her across the yard.

191

Chapter Eighteen

She led Ginny through the cold winter night towards the lighted windows of the house in front. Peggy would never be able to express to her aunt the gratitude that she felt for her. Mary was the one person Peggy had come to rely on and could bring a smile to her face during the worst of the days that surrounded them. The terror hadn't been as strong since they'd moved in the house behind. The few days that she spent alone with her mother after the first disappearance had filled Peggy with a fear that she continued to carry and for three days she used a bucket in the bedroom to relieve herself during the hours her daddy was at the store. She'd been afraid to leave her mother long enough to go to the outhouse and when she talked to Mary about it she was told that it would take the whole family to do what she was trying to do by herself.

"If you bring your mother and come in here, your daddy will come too. Don't let him stick you out there in the country trying to take care of Ginny by yourself! It took the whole family to watch after her when she got like this before."

Mary had been right. Ginny could disappear in the time that it took someone to walk into the next room and return. The last few weeks, she'd been getting harder to manage and had started talking about a man who came to see her. She would tell who ever was listening, that he was going to return for her and that she would have to leave with him when he did. She would be sitting frozen in a chair when suddenly she would try to dart out the door.

Ben drank more and more as the weeks passed while he watched Ginny slip farther and farther away. He fought the urge to run and thought back to the years before when she left. He recalled the times that he silently pleaded with her to return, or at least take him with her wherever it was that she went.

Friday after Thanksgiving, Peggy carried the trash out on her way to work. The aluminum trays that'd held the frozen turkey dinners of the day before crunched under the weight of her foot as she pushed them down towards the bottom of the can. The ground was white with frost when she made her way down the driveway towards the road that would take her to work.

Early in the afternoon a friend stopped by the store to purchase laundry soap and bleach.

"What time do you get off work? Would you wanna go to the Laundromat with me? We could go uptown afterwards."

"I'll have to ask but I'll bet that Roger would be happy

about not having to take me to do the laundry and come back to pick me up."

"I'll stop by your house in about an hour. If you can't go this week then maybe you can next time."

Two hours later, Peggy was sitting on the folding table at the Wash 'n Dry waiting for the washers to finish spinning. It was the first time that she'd been away from home with someone her own age that wasn't her brother.

"What time do you need to be home?"

Ben was sitting on the edge of the bed when Peggy opened the kitchen door hours later. He continued to turn over the cards from the deck that he held in his hand. Roger appeared in the doorway of the front room.

"Now that you're home safe, I'm goin' to bed."

Peggy carried the two baskets of clean laundry in from the back porch and set them down at the end of the bed where her father still sat. The bulb hanging from the ceiling in the kitchen cast its light on the cards spread out on the bed and one side of his face.

"Did you have a good time tonight?"

"Daddy I didn't do anything wrong. We just went uptown and hung out with some of the other kids."

He didn't respond, nor did he remove his eyes from the game still in process when she lay down beside her mother and placed her arm around the sleeping form. Hopefully, if Ginny tried to get out of bed during the night the movement against Peggy's arm would wake her. As Ben's drinking increased, the sleep that it induced grew deeper and Peggy didn't trust him to wake up if her mother decided to take a walk in the middle of the night.

"Good night Daddy."

Chapter Nineteen

"What do you think?"

"Well...I think that angel has probably seen better days. Are you really going to wrap those things that you bought for yourself?"

"What do you think? And if you don't quit picking, I might even wrap that sweater that you're wearing. By the way, thanks for the tree."

She stood back from the tree to get a better view. The small white lights appeared almost bashful tucked into the heavy branches of the spruce. This was the first tree that Peggy had ever decorated and she couldn't remember having a tree at home before. Pushing a couple of the lights farther into the branches, she straightened the angel one last time.

195

Across the Footbridge

"Now you stay put! The last thing that this family needs is a 'fallen angel'."

Her boss's sister-in-law had given her the box of lights and ornaments two days earlier and Roger bought the tree for her for Christmas. The day before she'd gone to town and spent the money that she'd earned for the last week on gifts for the rest of the family. She'd purchased a purse and a pair of boots for herself and Roger had been teasing her since she told him that she was going to wrap them and place them under the tree with the other presents.

Peggy gathered the decorations that she was taking to Mary and unplugged the tree lights. Her mother and father were sitting on her aunt's couch when she let herself in Maggie's front door.

"Mary, here's the decorations for the kids. Daddy, I'll be home a little after ten."

Ben's eyes never left the screen of the television and he had avoided any conversation with Peggy since she'd gone out with her friend the week before.

The roofs of the houses that she passed that Sunday afternoon held the white of the frost of the night before. She thought of the families that were huddled inside, watching football games or sitting down to Sunday dinner. She picked up her pace as the store came into sight.

...

December 8, 1970:

Mary had gone to Ginny's to borrow two eggs for a cake. When she was within sight of the back porch, she saw Ben rummaging through the dirty clothes. He jumped when he heard her footsteps on the frozen ground and hurriedly shoved the underwear he'd been looking at into the tub of the old washer and replaced the lid.

Three days later Peggy discovered him on the back porch with a pair of her panties in his hand.

"Daddy, what are you doing?"

She watched the crimson color creep upward from his collar then spread to cover his face. He replaced the dirty clothes that were scattered around his feet before he answered.

"Don't you think that I don't know what you were doing out till all hours of the morning."

The heat of anger and embarrassment flooded through her and she turned and walked away. The burden of humiliation that Peggy carried to work that morning outweighed all of the pain of the last few months. And to think that she'd dropped out of school so she could go to work to support his drinking habit. By the time she reached the front of the store a wall was forming around her heart, a wall that would isolate her from her father.

Ben put the dirty clothes back in the tub of the washer, set the lid in place and let himself in the house. He passed the bed where his wife lay on his way to the couch where he removed the half-gallon jug from its hiding place. When he replaced the lid on the wine, he knew that he was only doing what any man trying to bring up a teen-age girl alone would do.

. . .

The baby on Becky's lap was eight months old. His brother stood by his mother's knee watching the lights on the tree. Ginny was sitting at the other side of the room fiddling with a package in her lap.

Across the Footbridge

"Here Mommy, I'll help you with the wrapping, I can't wait to see what Santa brought."

Peggy removed the wrapping from the gift that Ginny's grandsons had just presented to her.

"Oh look Mommy, it's a new sweater! Grandma loves it, don't you Grandma?"

A few minutes later, Eddie carried one of his sons and Becky carried the other on their way to their car.

"Merry Christmas!"

...

Liphee was upset about the deterioration she saw in Ginny. The vacant look in her eyes was the same one she'd witnessed years before. Mary relayed the details of the trip to the hospital months before. Both were concerned about Ben's drinking.

When Liphee returned to Kentucky for Christmas, she wasn't sure if Ginny would remember the time that she spent with her or not. She was torn between the family she would leave the next day, and her life that was now more than three hundred miles north. Maggie cried when the car pulled out of the driveway the next morning.

"Mary, I'm afraid the next time we see her it'll be for a funeral."

Mary and George shared the same oppressive feeling that their mother had just put into words.

"Maybe, it's just the fact that we know how long she can be sick before she gets better."

"Maybe."

Each day Ginny seemed to withdraw a little further away from the family. Sometimes she carried on

198

conversations with people that only she could see and other times, she fought the locks on the doors and whoever tried to prevent her from leaving. The sight of Ben leading her down the path between the two houses became a familiar sight to the neighbors. Two weeks after Christmas, she again escaped the eyes that watched her and was missing for more than five hours. She returned by herself with a renewed determination to rejoin the man that she said she'd been with.

"He said that I couldn't go this time!"

"Ginny, who were you with?"

"I was with him…an' he's coming back to git me."

She weighed no more than a hundred pounds and the constant tension of her inner struggle was visible in the rigid stance of her body and the jerky movements in her limbs. Peggy hugged her mother close, feeling the distance that separated them, a distance that was growing wider each day.

With her renewed determination to join the person who played at the edges of her mind, Ginny became more difficult to confine and the doors were now locked when someone was in the room with her. During her rational moments, she started to speak of ending her life.

He pounded the last nail into the lid of the wooden box that covered the well in the back yard of the landlady's house. The spigot protruding from the side of her house provided water for the four houses that she collected rent for and she had suggested that Ben secure the lid on the old well box, *just in case*. Peggy watched her father bury the head of the last nail into the wood before he tried to pry the lid off with his hands. It didn't budge.

...

Across the Footbridge

January 18, 1971

"What time do you get off tonight?"

"Ten o'clock."

"I'll be back then."

She was pulling the last of the day's tape out of the register when she heard the bell on the front door.

"Ready?"

"As soon as I take the money to the back."

He watched Peggy pick up the cigar box from the counter and carry it to the door at the back of the store. She tapped on the glass. A few seconds later the door opened and a hand reached for the box.

Peggy turned off the lights and turned the lock on the front door as they left.

"What time do you gotta be home?"

"I don't have a set time, but I don't want to be out too late. Daddy's drinking more and she's getting harder to manage."

Fifteen minutes later he pulled the car into the open spot at the end of the lot and motioned for the carhop.

"Two small cokes, please."

He turned to face Peggy before he slid across the seat.

"You know it would be nice to go out on a real date sometime."

"I know."

Peggy leaned towards the warmth of the young man who'd been taking her home for almost three weeks.

Forty minutes later, he turned the car around at the back of Peggy's house before bringing it to a stop a few feet from the kitchen porch. He reached across her to open the car door.

"You know, one of these days you're gonna have to make a decision. If I'm gonna date you...I want to take you places and spend time with you. I understand about your mother, and I understand that you've never had sex before. You have to understand that I'm ready for a relationship. I'm not one of the kids that hang out in the backroom at the store. I've been to Nam, and I've played their games. You think about it and when you're ready for a relationship then you give me a call."

Ben heard the slam of the car door and the sound of gravel crunching before he heard Peggy unbolting the outside lock on the kitchen door.

"I know why that boy left here so upset!"

"That boy left here upset because I won't do what you've already accused me of doing! But you're not the reason that I don't. I don't wanna end up pregnant and stuck here in this hell hole for the rest of my life!"

Peggy heard the gurgling from the other room after she laid her head on the pillow and she was still awake when Roger let himself in the front door an hour later. She heard the creaking of the old springs sagging under his body as he settled down on the couch that had been his bed since they'd moved from the country. The last sounds she heard were snores coming from her father's bed across the room.

"Peggy Ann, are you still seeing that boy from up the road?"

"No. Mary, do you ever regret getting married?"

Across the Footbridge

"No, I wouldn't have my kids, an' besides... it wasn't all bad."

She was Peggy's best friend and the years that separated them in age were erased during the last months. Mary helped Peggy through the days of caring for her mother. Peggy helped her through the days of caring for the kids that now tagged after her. George had watched another sister's children grow from infants into toddlers.

Ginny sat staring at some unseen object while her family moved around her. The pain of her inner turmoil was becoming more evident and sometimes her eyes darted about the room searching for some mysterious object. At other times her struggle was visible in her eyes as some inner force continued to lure her into the hidden world that no one but she could see. Then, there were the times that she pleaded with her husband.

"Ben, help me...please!"

It was a broken man who pulled her hands away from their grasp on his shirt. She had implored him for days to help her end her life.

"Come on Ginny, let's go up to your mother's."

Five minutes later, he returned to open the front door. He reached behind the couch for his bottle before he sat down to bury his face in his hands as he wept. He cried for the woman he'd loved so many years before and he cried for the man that he'd been then. It was fifteen minutes later when he wiped his face on his shirtsleeve and returned the bottle to its hiding place before he closed the door and made his way back across the yard.

Across the Footbridge

Chapter Twenty

The piano notes died away as the sound of a ball striking a side pocket ended the game. Floyd Kramer's 'The Last Date' had played three spins on the jukebox in thc last hour. She watched a familiar hand remove the change from the window ledge before Roger appeared in the doorway of the poolroom.

She was pulling the day's tape out of the register as Eddie walked around the partition that had separated them.

"If you want Roger, you can go on home. I'll stick around and take her home."

Five minutes later Peggy pulled the door shut on the

203

store and ran towards Eddie's car that was waiting and warm. The ride was quick and silent and he delivered her to the back door.

"Thanks for the ride. Tell Becky and the boys hello."

Peggy hurried inside to get away from the frigid temperature. The plastic covering the inside of the kitchen window held the pattern of the latest melting. The drips made it almost to the bottom each day before the sun faded and left the water to freeze into a solid piece of ice that was now almost two inches high. The house was quiet when she turned out the kitchen light to undress and scoot in beside her mother. She heard the squeak of the couch springs in the other room after she closed her eyes.

Eddie looked at the gallon of milk on the seat beside him then turned his car in the opposite direction of home. He drove out past the house by the bridge and turned right. He followed the road over the railroad tracks and around past the fishing hole that he used to take Larry to when they were kids. Ten minutes later the road came to a tee and he turned right. Three minutes later he pulled the car to a stop in front of the house. He placed the milk that he'd gone to get hours before in the refrigerator before he crawled in beside his sleeping wife.

Becky felt the mattress move when Eddie eased his body between the sheets. She had waited three hours for him to return from the store. She knew something was bothering him and she hoped that it wasn't her.

Roger put the last load of dry-cleaning in the dryer before he went to the backroom to bring up hangers for the next day. He dreaded going home and he was tired of going out every evening. Maybe... he'd just go to his grandmother's

Across the Footbridge

house and visit with his uncle.

George had bought a tape recorder a few weeks before and had started several family feuds before the others stopped discussing the rest of the family with him. That week he had made up and recorded several songs that he was eager to play for his favorite nephew. Roger smiled as he thought of the content of the tapes that George kept under guard.

George worked enough to help his mother with the groceries and keep himself in wine on the weekends. He had acquired an admirer in the last few months, a widow ten years his senior and forty pounds heavier. She'd been pursuing him with an undoubting passion. Without her knowledge or consent, George had recorded several of their private conversations for the entertainment of his nephew. Maggie fussed at her son when he was home almost as much as she fussed about him when he was gone and as he had done when they were young and hungry, George tried to distract his niece and nephew from the pain that surrounded them.

"George! You shouldn't lead that woman on. She really cares about you!"

"I know Mommy, I'm gonna talk to her tonight."

Mary checked on the last child in the last bed. Everyone was asleep, finally. She returned to the front room to pick up the scattered toys. She was only thirty-one years old, but the last six months seemed thirty years long, and one horribly long day at the same time. The struggle of bringing up three children on next to nothing was at one time hard for her to accept. That was before she was exposed to Ginny's daily fight with her own private hell, the comparison making her life appear easy. Mary could recall some of the years before when

Ginny was sick though she'd been a child herself at the time. Most of her memories were of time spent trying to occupy her nephews while the rest of the family cared for Ginny. This time, Mary was the sister who held to Ginny's arm, preventing her from walking in front of a car she didn't see. It was Mary who watched as the disease that removed her sister from her, also pulled at her mother. Because Maggie was slowly giving in to the stress that had physically handicapped her years before, she was spending a large portion of her days in bed.

George was going to spend the evening with Berniece. Mary watched him remove his recorder from its hiding place and slip it into his coat pocket before he headed out into the night. She was waiting for the commotion that was bound to erupt when he got caught.

Mary thought back to the conversation that she'd had with Peggy earlier that week. Mary was a virgin when she met the man living in the house Liphee bought after Paul died and he was ten years older than she was. She'd slipped away in the evenings to meet him on the tracks that separated the two roads where they lived. Maggie had been upset when she heard from one of the neighbors that Mary was slipping around with a divorced man. But by the time the gossip traveled through the neighborhood to reach Maggie's ears, Mary was pregnant. Now, ten years and four children later, she identified with the similar position her niece was in. Peggy was tied to her mother and Mary was tied to her children. Mary never regretted getting married but did regret that the marriage hadn't worked out as she had hoped.

...

Across the Footbridge

Three hundred and thirty miles away Liphee tucked her son in for the night while four doors away, Norma Rhodes leaned into her oven, the sugar she sifted through her fingers falling to cover the golden tops of three pies. The aroma drifted into the next room capturing the attention of her husband. Ivan followed the smell to find himself looking over his wife's stooped shoulder. She jumped with a pinch of crust still clamped between one finger and thumb.

"Old man! Why do you always sneak up on me like that?"

He relieved his wife of the crust in her fingers, before attacking her rear-end with his free hand.

"You haven't made this many pies since we closed the restaurant. I thought maybe you were trying to court me again."

"You should realize that I have more sense than that. The pies are for Michael. That boy can sure put away his grandma's pies."

Ivan and Norma Rhodes accepted Liphee and Michael, as they would have their own blood relatives. For fifteen years, the couple owned and operated a restaurant and bar in a small town about forty miles south. Ivan managed the restaurant and Norma handled the bar. He played the role of bouncer for her when the occasion arose, and in return she provided his customers with fresh baked pies. It'd been four years since they'd sold the business and relocated to a mobile home park on the edge of a small lake.

The interior of their home was a true reflection of the couple. One end of the living room was overflowing with fishing and hunting paraphernalia and two pairs of insulated rubber boots had taken up year-round residence in front of the kitchen door. One wall in the living room appeared to have been designed by the original ark builder with mounted deer heads and a stuffed raccoon that looked down on petrified fish and stuffed ducks. One corner of the room was rounded with the fishing poles that leaned into it while a wide assortment of fake insects tied to hooks had their heads buried in two of the four hats on the hall tree. Amidst all this, were curio cabinets filled to overflowing with delicate china and fragile collectibles. Ivan always said if it came in twos, Norma had to collect it. Evidence of her skill with a hook and yarn was visible on the back of every chair and bed and the remnants of three daily papers were strewn between the two easy chairs that were placed at the same angle. Ivan always said, she had to see everything at the same time he did, or before him. Norma always said, "Hush up, old man!"

The easy companionship between the two was visible beneath the crusty exterior they wrapped their relationship in and Michael relished the position of being an object of their rivalry. For every homemade pie that Norma produced, Ivan provided a little something that Michael shouldn't tell his mom or grandma about and Norma always came back with a bribe to find out what the 'ornery old man' was up to now.

Norma and Ivan worked to make Michael's adjustment to his new surroundings as smooth as possible because they wanted Liphee and her son to remain in Indiana. At least three times a week, Norma baked one of Michael's favorite desserts and at least three times a week, Liphee carried something she cooked special for Ivan down the lane that separated the two

Across the Footbridge

homes.

Norma's son, John Meeks, was a grown man when she met and married Ivan who was ten years younger and had never had children of his own. Ivan didn't take a particular liking to either of his stepchildren but he and Norma were both taken with Liphee and Michael. On the weeks that the poverty of the South wasn't enough to keep Liphee in Indiana, her husband's parents were.

As Norma moved her pies from the oven to the counter, Liphee struggled with the temptation to go south. Her years of caring for her family had instilled a sense of responsibility in her that was difficult to shed. On nights like this, she often walked the path to Norma's backdoor. An hour with the couple usually gave her the strength to go home and appreciate the fact that she wasn't as alone as she felt. The smiles Ivan always planted on her face would still be visible when Liphee turned the lights out for the night.

After their return from Kentucky the year before, John found a job with a factory that produced by-products for the automotive industry and Liphee managed a small dry-cleaners in a little town ten miles north. John worked evenings at the factory while Liphee and Michael spent most of their time as they had after Paul died, in the company of family that now included Ivan and Norma.

Ivan saw Liphee's face through the window in the kitchen door and had his hand raised to motion her inside before she raised one of hers to knock. The odor of fresh brewed coffee and homemade pies greeted her when she entered the cluttered kitchen and Ivan moved from the recliner in the front room to the chair at the end of the kitchen table.

His wide face was open and friendly.

"Well now, don't tell me the scent of those pies drifted all the way up to your house."

"Hush up old man! I told Michael to have his mother come pick his dessert up tonight, before the old fart got his paws into them."

Forty minutes later, Ivan watched Liphee's back disappear into the night. He turned the lock on the kitchen door then reached for his wife.

"I worry about her and the boy. I know most of the time her thoughts are with her family down south."

"I know old man."

Maggie lay with her youngest granddaughter's small hand resting on the space over her heart. She thought back to the times she'd fallen asleep with her hand on Charley's. The small girl at her side would never know the man who still lived in Maggie's heart. She often thought that things would have been different, if only he had lived. She heard George open the door and enter the darkened house.

"Oh God, please watch over my first born, and tell her daddy that I miss him."

George overheard his mother's last conversation of the day.

"Me too, Lord."

Across the Footbridge

Chapter Twenty-one

With the pull of the knob, the last ball of the game was released. Four bells, the sound of a buzzer, and a hand thumping the side of the pinball machine could be heard over the noise of fifteen washers in various stages of cycling. Peggy looked up from the towels she was folding in time to see him smack the machine one last time before he walked away.

"These ready to go?"

The fingers on the hands reaching for the basket showed the tension in their owner who had chewed the nails into stubby ends. Roger carried the basket out of the building and placed it in the backseat of his car. It was the first Sunday of February 1971 and Peggy needed to be at work in less than an hour. Her shifts rotated from week to week because the proprietor of the store had employed enough teen-agers through the years to realize that none of them wanted to work Saturday nights, or come in on Sunday mornings if they didn't. He adjusted the schedule accordingly.

Roger had dropped Peggy and two baskets of dirty clothes at the laundromat, two hours before. He went back home to wait the hour and half that she told him she'd need to finish her weekly chore. Peggy had to wait in line for washers and then wait again for available dryers so when Roger returned for her she was just removing the first clothes from the dryer.

Five minutes later, she was seated in the front seat of his car, her arms filled with clothes on hangers. The warm material blocked her from the outdoor temperature that hovered at twenty degrees. The patch of frost that Roger cleared from his windshield earlier was again freezing into new ice formations.

"I'll drop the laundry off an' then I'll take you to work if you want."

"Thanks."

No two of Ginny's four children had discussed the illness that had crept back into their mother's life. Roger and Peggy lived with the monster without identifying it while silently acknowledging the presence disrupting both of their teen-age lives. If one went out in the evening then the other stayed home yet they never discussed the reason they felt one of them should be home every evening... and they never discussed the horror of what their mother's illness was doing to their father.

Two miles away, Eddie struggled with his own knowledge of what was happening. Three times in the last few months, he'd been called to come help with the search and he'd driven through the surrounding neighborhoods as his eyes searched the ditch lines and back yards of the houses he passed. The creek he and his brothers played in as children wound through the area where his parents now lived on its path to the river a few miles away. Usually, the creek was nothing more than a trickle as it passed between his parents' home and the store where his sister worked. But the banks on either side were several feet high from the swell of the current after the spring rains. The many places his mother could hide made any attempt at finding her almost assured to be fruitless. The last time she disappeared, she was seen walking out of the tunnel where the road crossed over the tracks at the end of the adjoining road. Each family member had felt relief that a train hadn't been moving down the tracks at the time.

Eddie had come to dread the ringing of the phone and he struggled with his feelings, as he tried to resolve the anger that was building in him. Lately, he had started easing the sharpness of the pain with occasional swallows of whiskey. Becky silently watched the effects of the unknown tear at the fibers of her marriage. The week before, she had suggested to Eddie that they leave the boys and go out for an evening. Could they go to out to dinner and maybe a movie?

"Maybe your mom would like to come here and stay with the boys."

The next day, he asked Peggy if she'd be free to baby-sit on Saturday night. Becky never knew that Eddie couldn't leave the children alone with his mother. She thought Peggy came along because she didn't want to stay home alone. Eddie hurried Becky out to the car when he returned with his mother and sister and then left the motor running on his car when they returned. He had his mother and sister out of the house in less than two minutes. When Eddie asked Peggy how things had gone, Becky assumed that he was asking about the two sleeping boys in the back bedroom.

On the drive home from the laundromat, Roger inquired about the evening before.

"How did things go at Eddie's last night?"

"Fine, the boys were asleep when we got there. We came home as soon as they returned."

Ben and Ginny were sitting in the front room when they carried the baskets into the house.

"Mommy did you have something to eat while I was gone?"

"I ...think so."

Fifteen minutes later, Peggy was behind the register and Roger was dropping nickels into the jukebox.

...

"Do you wanna try a little? It might make you feel better."

She stared at the bottle he held in front of her but she didn't see him or the bottle, everything was removed. She was looking out through the long tunnel before she began to run. She had to get out...

The jug slipped from his hand as she moved past him.

"I've got to get out of here! He's behind me!"

Across the Footbridge

Ben caught her at the end of the front porch. He had forgotten to bolt the front door when he went to the outhouse. Ginny fought his hands as they tried to restrain her. They were the hands from the tunnel. Hands that kept drawing her into its depth.

"No! No! Noooo!"

He managed to push her through the front door and lock it before he turned around to find her trembling in front of him. Her arms were crossed in front of her as her eyes darted about the room, searching for something ... He bent down and picked up the jug and tipped it to his mouth while she turned her attention to something that moved on the wall behind his head. Roger returned home an hour later to find his father sitting on the couch, just watching, as his mother paced, back and forth through the rooms of the little house.

George and Berniece were sitting on Maggie's couch, both of their laps filled with sticky faced children. She continued to return to Maggie's house each day with something good that she wanted to share with the little ones. Mary had started dropping hints that maybe the little ones could use fewer candy bars and a little more milk in their diet.

"You know, I get awfully lonely in that big house all by myself."

George was starting to feel smothered by the pressure she steadily applied. The night before she proposed.

"Berniece, I told you last night that I don't want to get married. I know that your husband left you enough money to support both of us but you wouldn't be very happy when I took a notion to see a different state, or decided my family needed me on a night that you were feeling lonely."

Across the Footbridge

Ben overheard the conversation. It ain't right, he told himself on the walk through the yard an hour later.

"Berniece is a fine woman, and George wouldn't ever have to hit a lick at nothing again. I need a woman... and the one I got don't know I'm in the world an' here he's got a fine woman like Berniece, and he don't want her. It's enough to drive a man to drink."

Anger at the unfairness of life was starting to grow in him and each day was a repeat of the one before. The only visible change he could see was in the soap operas that filled the afternoon hours. Even the bad situations on them turned around eventually. Ben had started discussing the lives on the screen as if the characters portrayed, were real people he had come to know and he usually discussed Friday's cliffhanger most of the weekend.

The people that surrounded Ginny could feel the effects of the pressure of the vacuum that continued to draw her towards it. Peggy was replacing her feelings of fear with the sharp edge of hate. She hated the poverty, and hated the wine that numbed her father from the reality that she still had to live with. She went through the daily motions of taking care of the house. Each day, when her shift at the store ended, she counted the hours until she could return but time seemed to be standing still.

The first week of March brought sunshine and fifty-degree temperatures and overnight, tiny buds appeared on the highest limbs of the trees. Birds could be heard quarreling, as they scavenged the thawing ground in search of worms and bugs. The walk to work and back became something that Peggy looked forward to again. It had been two months since she saw him last. He showed up five minutes before closing time.

"Do you need a ride home?"

...

They sat in the parking lot for more than hour. Nothing had changed in her life since they had talked and he was leaving the next day. He had re-enlisted. When he dropped her in front of her door he asked if he could look her up when he came home on leave.

Peggy lay in bed that night thinking of him, and why he had returned. For an entire week after he took her home the last time, she considered becoming involved with him. She even considered trying to get pregnant because she knew that he would have married her. She would be leaving for Virginia tomorrow, if she had followed through with her plan. Peggy looked at her mother's still form lying in the bed beside her.

"I'm sorry Mommy...but I don't know how much more of this I can take."

Ginny didn't hear the words her daughter spoke in the night because she was somewhere else. She was traveling through the tunnel and the man with the long white beard was in front of her. Before she reached the end where the light was bright and warm, he made her turn around and go back. But he told her that he would return and she could go with him when he did.

"He said he'd be back for me. I can go with him when he comes back for me."

Peggy was asleep and didn't hear the words Ginny whispered in the dark house.

The second week of March the sunshine disappeared

behind clouds that accumulated for two days before the first drop of rain splattered against the plastic on the kitchen window. Peggy was at work when the skies opened up so Roger picked her up at closing time. They were both drenched by the time they ran the distance between his car and the back porch. By morning, the worst of the storm had passed to the south leaving a slow steady rain falling in its place. Within two days the water in the creek could be seen from the road and by the end of the week, the ground had absorbed as much as it could hold, leaving Ben's back yard under water.

The water ran down the sides of the hills towards the creek that widened with each mile that it traveled. The water rushing through the culverts under the roads was the color of wet cement and the Ohio River continued to climb towards the floodwalls that surrounded most of the downtown area. Ben stood under the shelter of the porch roof, looking out into the gray drizzle. The house set in one of the lowest spots in the area and for thirty feet on either side, all he could see was the spats of raindrops landing on the standing water. He made paths through the yard with rocks and boards. The water had slowly risen to cover the last bridge he built when the rain stopped on the first day of spring, March 21, 1971, the twenty-first anniversary of Larry's birth.

The house smelled of fungi and wet wood. The water slowly receded to display irregular splotches of mud before the sun extracted the water back towards the heavens. Ben left the doors of the house standing open during the times that he and Ginny went to her mother's house so the mild breeze could circulate through the rooms and remove some of the dampness that clung to the interior walls. The bottoms of

Across the Footbridge

everyone's shoes looked as if they had all been dipped in the same vat of wet thin cement while the two weeks of confinement and absence of sunlight had tightened the lines of stress that had appeared in everyone's brows.

Mary's kids slept away the majority of the long dark afternoons and their wakeful nights became tiring to the adults in the house. George hadn't worked since the rain began. On March 25, he started mixing cement for the contractor who was building the new community building at the edge of town. He returned home that evening tired and happy from spending a full day in the sunshine. The croaking of frogs was heard for the first time since the previous summer.

The moisture in the air took on a more solid form the further north you traveled. Liphee had been snowed in for three days, when she woke to find the glare of sunlight reflecting off snowdrifts that surrounded three sides of her house. By late afternoon, most of the main roads had been plowed open and two days later the schools reopened their doors for the first time in nine days. On Friday, March 25, she returned to work and Michael returned to school.

Her car was following the school bus that afternoon when it opened its doors to release Michael for two more days of freedom. He helped her carry in the bags of food that she had bought in preparation of another blizzard.

On Sunday, March 27, the temperature climbed to seventy-one degrees and Mary opened the front door trying to chase more of the dampness out of the house. On Saturday night, George took part of his Friday's earnings and bought a few hours of drunken oblivion. Sunday morning he counted his money.

Across the Footbridge

"If you make a list of what you need from the store, I'll go get it before I decide to spend the rest of the money in my pocket on more wine."

Mary wrote down what she needed for the days remaining till her support check would arrive. A little after one, George pushed the list in his pant's pocket and left.

Peggy saw George walking down the road when she and her mother went to Maggie's. He returned about fifteen minutes later and set a bag of groceries down on the porch, then sat down beside it. He rested for a few minutes before he picked up the bag and carried it through the open door.

"Here, Mary take these, I don't feel good."

She took the groceries and started towards the kitchen and got as far as the doorway leading into the next room when she turned around to ask him a question.

He'd sat down in the closest chair and she saw his pupils drift towards his forehead.

She dropped the bag and ran to his side.

"George!" "Oh my God, Peggy go get your dad and call for an ambulance!"

Ginny and three young children stood there, watching in silence...

Peggy ran to the landlady's house to call for an ambulance then went home to get her father. Three minutes later, Ben stood with his hand on George's neck. He was still touching him when the EMT's came through the door. Ben followed the stretcher into the back of the ambulance.

...

Norma was in the bedroom when the phone rang. She returned to the front room as Ivan replaced the receiver.

"Who was on the phone old man?"

"We'd better find out if John's home. He'll need to be with Liphee when we tell her that her brother just died."

Chapter Twenty-two

His knuckles had taken on the appearance of chicken bones with the knuckles standing out in sharp contrast to the weathered skin on the backs of his hands and exposed wrists. For the past three hours he had watched the centerline on the highway, the road back home. Shelly moved the sleeping baby into a different position. Larry hadn't spoken since they stopped to get gas and use the toilet at a gas station seventy miles behind. He'd been quiet since Liphee and John informed him of his uncle's death and that they needed to be at the funeral home on Monday morning to make arrangements. It was almost noon, the day after George Sexton died from heart failure.

...

Roger followed the ambulance as it sped towards the emergency entrance of the hospital. Forty minutes later, he and Ben returned. Roger's eyes were swollen and red. George was gone. Maggie's son had returned home to die as he'd promised.

Ginny was struggling to find her way out of the darkness.

"Mary, our brother died?"

Maggie lay facing a wall, shudders moving through her body as she released her last son. She hadn't spoken since the ambulance carried George away. Mary placed the call to John's parents an hour after Ben and Roger returned with George's wallet and fifty-three cents. The wallet contained a social security card, a sliver of a ribbon that had been part of the flowers that lay on his father's casket, and a one-dollar bill. Liphee didn't have a phone so Mary was relieved of the burden of informing her of their brother's death.

...

Liphee followed the undertaker into his office after she had selected clothing, a vault, and a coffin lined in the palest green. The funeral director discretely showed her the lowest priced wares available to him and she ran her hand over the simulated wood-grain.

"Is this cardboard?"

"No Mam, well actually it's made of a corrugated fiber."

"Is this all you have to show me?"

"I do have other selections in the front of the display

room...ahm... Did your brother have an insurance policy ...perhaps that I am unaware of?"

She swallowed back anger from years of practice.

"No! My brother had just what you thought he had. He died not owing anything to anybody and he had a dollar and fifty three cents left over."

She signed the necessary papers, after years of practice her signature still shaky. At ten thirty, she walked into her sister's house.

"Ginny, when I go home after the funeral I want you and Peggy Ann to go with me. I'm going to take you to a doctor up home. Okay?"

...

She had packed the suitcase while John and Michael took the car and filled it with gas and they were on the road an hour after Ivan and Norma received the call. For five of the eight hours that they traveled the night before, Liphee sat, staring into the darkness of her side window. What would she say to her mother?

It was almost midnight when the car moved across the bridge and they heard the movement of the swollen current as they passed over. Ten minutes later, the car stopped in front of Maggie's door.

The kids had fallen asleep an hour before and Mary, Maggie, and Roger were sitting, waiting. They heard the slam of a car door and the mumbled noise of voices. When Liphee opened the front door, Maggie broke. The tears she'd held back for more than ten hours seeping from the corners of her lids as she buried her head in her daughter's arms. Roger went to the kitchen to make coffee. It would be a long night.

He would be placed under a tree in the cemetery at the other edge of town. Did she want to bring him home for a day? No! The viewing was set for Tuesday, from two to four and six to eight. His nephews would bear the weight of his coffin.

When she walked into Ginny's house an hour after she left the funeral home, she felt the space of thirty years fade. The bed was different and the air inside the room was warm this time, but when she looked at the middle-aged woman huddled in the middle of a bed, Liphee was thirteen again. This time Pappy was gone and it was up to her.

"I wanna take Ginny and Peggy Ann back with me. Do ya understand?"

They were standing on the front porch and Ben looked at the lock that he'd placed on the outside of the door.

"Liphee, she's the only woman that I ever really loved."

It was after five when Larry turned his car into the driveway leading to his parents' back door. His back was sore from the tension of the long drive, the reason for the trip, and apprehension of facing his mother. Less than twenty minutes later his car was headed back out of the drive.

He'd sat staring into the blue flames of the gas heater while Peggy urged their mother out of the bed in the next room. Ginny remained in the bed, staying in the tunnel that she'd entered early that morning. Less than twenty feet away, Larry struggled to absorb the impact of her rejection.

"Come on Sally, let's go!"

Across the Footbridge

Sally and Becky were waiting for their husbands to return. Becky's father had provided three sports coats for anyone that needed one. Eddie would wear the suit that he bought for his wedding when he carried his uncle two days later. Roger tried on the first jacket Becky handed to him.

"This will work."

An hour later, Eddie's car stopped in front of his house. The three brothers stood in the kitchen sharing the bottle of whiskey.

Some of the neighbors volunteered to keep the kids during the viewing and the funeral. Maggie was led to a car at one o'clock on Tuesday and taken to the funeral parlor where she sat at the end of her son's casket for three hours. Peggy stayed with Ginny during the afternoon viewing and Ben stayed with her that evening.

Some of the men who came worked with George years before in the mines and most of the faces were unfamiliar to his family. Each man stopped to relay a story of a night of drinking or a day from the past, with his family and for more than five hours people his family had never met came to say good-bye to him. That night his family relived his life through the stories they recalled and once again, he replaced their tears of grief with smiles, his last gift to his family.

The oppressive weight of family's grief surrounded her, trying to penetrate the walls of the tunnel that wrapped her in its darkness, and she fought against its force. She'd watched him leave. Why was he going into the tunnel instead of her?

"Mary, I wanna go be with our brother."

Ginny's words pierced the cloud of grief.

Across the Footbridge

"Whatta ya mean, you wanna go be with George?"

She had slipped back into the darkness.

The heat woke Peggy Wednesday morning and she threw the blankets back, her neck stiff as she tried to raise her head off the pillow. She tried to swallow. Her tongue was the size of the pillow that she turned trying to find the coolness of the other side. Ginny was still asleep beside her. She moved her feet over the edge of the bed but the weight of her body pulled her back. An hour later, she made it to the water bucket in the next room. Her bones had softened during the night and her knees struggled under the weight of her body. Her forehead was damp and her eyes glassy from the fever.

Sometime later, Liphee stood looking down at her niece.

"Honey, don't you feel like going to the funeral?"

She closed her eyes and within seconds three hours had passed. Her uncle was buried and her family had returned from his funeral. Liphee was talking to her again.

"Peggy, have you ate or drank anything today?"

"I don't think I can swallow. Where's Mommy?"

Ginny returned to find her daughter sprawled across the bed, her head constantly searching for a cool spot on the pillow. Ben saw the recognition in her eyes and wondered how long she would stay?

"If something happens to me, I want you to promise me that you'll come back and get her."

The two sisters looked at the girl lying on the bed. Peggy's face was flushed, her neck swollen. Liphee placed a hand on the hot dry skin and discovered that the aspirin that she gave her a half-hour before was starting to react.

"Nothing's going to happen to you. Remember, you're both going home with me tomorrow."

"Just promise me, please? I don't want her left here with Ben!"

They had returned from the cemetery an hour before. Roger and John helped Maggie move from the car to the bed where she continued to mourn her son's death while Mary went to the neighbor's to bring her children home and Liphee went to the house behind. Larry and Shelly left the cemetery and headed for the highway. He asked Roger to say good-bye to his father and sister for him.

Ginny was drinking a cup of coffee when Liphee entered the house.

"Peggy's sick."

The sight of Ginny coherent eased some of the pain of her brother's death. Liphee turned to Ben for an explanation.

"She came around about an hour ago. She asked where everyone was, an' she wanted a cup of coffee. Maybe she's gonna be all right."

He left his wife's side for the first time that day and followed the path to the outhouse before he circled around to stop and take a drink from the bottle behind the seat in the truck. When he returned fifteen minutes later, her eyes were focused on the wall above Liphee's head as she watched the pattern on the wall move and take on different shapes before it formed itself into the shape of a tunnel.

Chapter Twenty-three

The paper bags filled with dirty clothes were put in last. Liphee's suitcase made an island in the middle of the trunk surrounded by all of the clothes that Peggy and Ginny owned. Two bags of dirty clothes, one bag of clean, and four items on hangers made up both wardrobes. Hopefully, after they got settled, her mother would improve and she'd be able to find a job. John had mentioned the possibility of her going back to school and Peggy recalled the conversation as she put Ben's dirty laundry back into the basket.

"Peggy, you really need to get back into school, cause if you stay in Indiana, you'll need your diploma to get a decent job. How would you feel about going back?"

Her mind had traveled back to the days that she'd spent sitting in the classrooms at the county high school and felt stirrings of the old dreams that she'd buried more than a year before.

"It'd be more'n I could hope for."

...

"Roger, I could've washed your and Daddy's clothes if you'd have taken me to do the laundry last night."

"I've washed more shirts than you can count. Besides, the women at work will press em' for me, an' I thought you was sick."

"I just told you that to get out of doing the laundry."

The trunk lid lowered. One last time Peggy went back through the house to see if she'd forgotten anything. The rooms looked as if they'd been neglected for more than the three days that she'd been sick. Dirty dishes were piled to overflowing in the sink. The water bucket was dry and the trash should have been taken out the day before. The beds looked as if they'd been made at instead of made up and her father's jug of wine was placed in plain view when she went through the front room. A thin layer of dust covered the tops of the furniture and one of the cushions was hanging over the edge of the couch. Without thinking, she bumped the cushion in passing.

"I'm glad I'm not gonna be here to see what it looks like after a few weeks!"

Peggy's words echoed through the empty rooms

...

Across the Footbridge

The top formation of the bridge was visible in John's rearview mirror and Peggy watched the last familiar sight fade with the miles. The highway was moving them north while she watched the hills pass between the silhouettes of her uncle and aunt's heads. For twelve miles, the car followed the road along the river before John aimed it into the traffic of another highway that would take them north and the river disappeared as hills rose on either side.

She felt the movement of the pavement under her seat, the constant vibration pulling at her consciousness. One by one, Peggy felt her muscles relax as they released the pent-up tension of the last year and a half. Liphee and John had lifted a lot of the heavy weight that she'd been carrying. She looked at her mother in the seat beside her.

Ginny eyes were focused on the back of John's head and she hadn't spoken since they started across the bridge more than an hour before. She had asked if they were going to buy wine.

Peggy watched the scenery move past her mother's profile, the road cutting through as if the hills were sticks of butter. The layers of earth that she'd studied in her fifth grade science class were revealed and unexpectedly she recalled the diagram in her textbook and the teacher who'd insisted her students memorize the table of layers. The next thing she saw was the front of a gas station. She'd slept for more than a hundred miles.

The bends of her legs were stiff and a sharp knife was wedged into her lower back. She leaned her head towards her knees stretching the cramped muscles. The hills had shrunk and the temperature had dropped another twenty degrees while she was asleep. Peggy ran towards the door at the side of the building and when she returned to the car Michael was sitting in the backseat with her mother and John motioned for her to sit in the front. For the next five hours she watched the transformation of hills dwindling to flat fields. She passed through towns with names she was familiar with and others with names out of a storybook. The hills receded so gradually that she couldn't recall the last one or the first flat field.

"What's that?"

"A soybean field."

"I didn't know there was that many people who ate Chinese food."

"There's not. Farmers grow it for cattle feed."

"How much farther?"

"About an hour or two."

Peggy's spirits lifted with each mile the road put between her and Kentucky. She'd forgotten how it felt to just be a kid but the only thing she'd have to do for the next two hours was breathe, no doors to lock, no meals to cook, no dishes to wash, and no groceries to bag. And, she wouldn't have to set her mind to wake if her mother moved in the bed beside her tonight. Liphee would help her and soon her mother would be okay.

Peggy felt a sharp stab of guilt for her light heart. She'd have never wished George dead, not even for a million dollars, but if he hadn't died then Liphee would still be in Indiana and Peggy would still be in Kentucky.

The tallest buildings she'd ever seen rose past the sidewalks and reached towards the skyline.

Across the Footbridge

"Where are we?"

"About forty miles from home."

The roads were all straight and level, each one appearing identical to the one before it. Houses stood at the ends of long driveways with cornfields reaching around both sides and back towards the horizon. Turning the steering wheel, John looked at Peggy.

"The next cornfield that you see will be across the road from our house."

The car stopped at the side of a small white house. When Peggy looked at a window high above her head, Liphee followed her gaze.

"That'll be where you and your mommy'll sleep."

The ground underneath her feet moved as she stood for the first time in more than four hours. She walked to stand in front of the house, snow crunching under her feet. The cornfield John promised was across the road with the left over stubble of last year's crops sticking through the snow. It was all that separated her from the skyline on the far side. She turned to take in the view of her new home and saw a small porch with an overhang extending out from the house, leading guests from the front walk to the entrance. The sidewalk would have been perfect a few years ago when she was into playing hopscotch and the one big tree in front of the house would provide shade in a few weeks. This would be the first house that she ever lived in with paint on the outside and plumbing on the inside. She watched the mist of steam coming from the pipe sticking up from the roof, no more building fires in a cold kitchen.

The yard was separated from the mobile home park by

a fence that ran the length of the property, the enclosure following the curve of the incline of back yard. Peggy's eyes followed the fence line till it abruptly stopped at the bottom of the hill. A smooth field of white was on the other side.

"Is that the lake?"

"It will be in a few weeks."

The backdoor opened into her aunt's kitchen where the tile on the floor was unblemished and the soft overhead lighting reflected off the surfaces of the toaster and glass doors on the stove that had two ovens. John pulled on a cord and the drapes in the dining room parted to reveal a view of the lake below while the pale light of the late afternoon flooded the room. Peggy carried the paper bags through the living room and up the stairway to the bedroom where Michael led her. Two bedrooms opened off the small hall at the top of the stairs and he showed her the one on the right.

"I'm glad that I won't have to sleep up here by myself anymore."

"Me too."

An hour later the bags were unpacked and the aromas of food and fresh coffee drifted up the stairway. Peggy turned from the view at the bedroom window filled with relief that it was finally behind her. She knew, as she'd known as a small girl, that Liphee would make everything all right.

Their first supper in Indiana was bacon and eggs. Peggy buttered the toast and poured coffee into the cups that Liphee placed on the table. While she'd been upstairs, John had put an extension in the table and when they sat down to supper, Peggy could see the houses across the lake. She hoped this wasn't a dream because if it was, she didn't want to wake.

Ginny sat at the table while her sister and daughter cleared away the evidence of the meal and Liphee showed Peggy the whereabouts of things she might need the next day. Peggy carried the dirty clothes to the basement. Tomorrow, she'd put them in the washer and dryer downstairs. At nine-thirty, she led Ginny up the stairs to her new bed.

It seemed strange having her mother across the room from her when she closed her eyes but she knew that John had bolted both of the doors for the night. Ginny was safe and Peggy could sleep.

She opened her eyes to find that the first tinges of dawn were bathing the room in an eerie light, the bed and room unfamiliar. She sat up sliding her feet between the sheets towards the cool floor. The bed across the room was empty, the house silent. She moved on bare feet to the window where she saw her mother through the bottom pane. The top of Ginny's head moved out of her view. Peggy yearned to return to the warm bed but reality brought her to full consciousness.

"Mommy's headed for the lake! Liphee stop her...."

The stairs were an unfamiliar obstacle path when she ran through the house, yelling for her aunt, uncle, cousin, for God, or anyone that would help. Everything slowed when she stepped onto the cold cement of the back porch.

She could see her at the edge of the lake and she was walking towards the water. Peggy opened her mouth to scream but the sound refused to come out. In an attempt to shed the panic inside taking control of her body, she ran down the steps, her feet hesitating to take the commands her brain issued. The weights tied to her ankles drug her down, her voice was uncooperative, her eyes the only parts of her body that didn't refuse to function. In silent horror, they watched her mother walk into the depths of the cold gray water.

"Mommy...!"

"Peggy, Peggy. Wake up!"

Liphee was shaking her and the cold winter air turned into the dry air of the bedroom in Kentucky. It was the morning after George's funeral.

The panic that the dream created had raised her blood pressure. Her skin was cool and moist and her throat was thick and useless for several minutes after she woke. Peggy sat on the edge of the bed trying to come back from the nightmare that'd removed her from Kentucky and removed her mother from her. Gradually, her heart rate slowed while Liphee stood beside the bed with her hand placed on Peggy's forehead.

"I think your fever is down. Are you sure that you'll be all right after I leave? We'll be back to get you and your mommy a week from Saturday."

The trip to Indiana had been postponed for a week because Peggy was too sick to travel. It was the last day of March and Mary and Maggie moved across the two roads and railroad tracks into Liphee's house because the painful memories of George's death followed them through the rooms of the house where he died. John and Liphee crossed over the bridge into Ohio at noon.

The days following a funeral is a time when surviving family members feel as if they are hanging suspended in midair. The planning of funeral arrangements and the reliving of memories, is their time of acceptance so that after the funeral, clocks start ticking again, meals are cooked and lives resume. The gapping hole left in their lives slowly starts to close.

The heavy cloud that'd hung over the family for the last four days didn't lift its heavy blanket of depression after George was buried and the finality, usually felt after a loved one is committed to the earth, was void.

Peggy stood inside the doorway watching the back of the car move out of her sight. She felt relief that her mother was in the room behind her instead of the car that was headed north. The dream she'd had earlier that day was so real that Peggy still carried some of the fear that she'd awaken from it with. That feeling mixed with the apprehension that was present in both houses.

The swollen glands felt like she had a warm grapefruit lodged at the back of her throat and what food she managed to swallow was tasteless. She gargled with warm salt water then peered at her throat in the mirror hanging over the kitchen sink. Her tongue looked like it had been dipped in something white as the blisters that'd formed in her throat spread into her mouth. Her temperature fluctuated through the afternoon hours and she struggled to swallow the soup Roger brought home that night.

Ben drank through the afternoon while Peggy slept. Ginny traveled through the tunnel; twice she returned to find her daughter asleep on the bed and her husband tipping back the jug as he tried to drain the last drops remaining in the bottle. Roger returned home from work at five-thirty. He left a few minutes later to go to the store.

Peggy fought the fatigue that'd settled in her bones as she walked to Mary's with her mother. Twenty minutes later, she was asleep on her grandmother's bed. At bedtime, Mary woke her and sent her home with Ginny.

The sounds of someone moving about the room pulled Peggy from the blanket of sleep and she opened her eyes and moved her hand to the other side of the bed. She felt the lump under the covers. Slowly, she pushed the covers from her body and replaced them once she was out of bed. Roger was making a bundle of his dirty clothes.

"I'm sorry about the laundry."

"Don't worry about it. Do you need me to take any of your stuff to the cleaners?"

"Nah, I haven't worn anything but the things I've slept in for almost a week. Maybe, if I don't feel better tomorrow, you might take some stuff for Mommy and Daddy. I hope I feel like going to the laundromat tonight."

Friday afternoon Peggy woke to find the house empty. The quiet seemed eerie in the dark room and she hurried out of the house and towards the path.

Maggie had remained quiet and in bed since she returned from George's funeral, only leaving the bed to go to the bathroom and walk to Liphee's house where Mary carried the kids and her clothes to the day before. Several times she had tried to coax herself out of bed but the air around her was heavy, the same as when she'd sat at Charlie's bed, waiting. That's what it felt like. They were all waiting for something tragic to happen. The tragedy had already happened but the feeling hadn't taken its scheduled leave.

Ben felt the same fears as his wife's family. He'd been

238

Across the Footbridge

across the tracks three times that day because something about Ginny's eyes brought a chill to his skin. She seemed to be alert but not in the same realm as the rest of them. Ben saw recognition in her eyes yet he couldn't find the object of her concentration. His jug was dry and the check wouldn't be in till the next day.

Liphee and John returned to work on Friday and Michael again returned to school for one day before he was dismissed for the weekend. Ivan and Norma waited for Liphee to share her grief with them. She'd been quiet since she returned from her brother's funeral but on Friday evening she followed the path to Norma's backdoor. Michael had gone to visit a friend after school. He needed to be free of his mother's grieving for a few hours.

"How are you doing?"

Ivan's voice carried from the front room to greet her when she entered the kitchen. An hour later, he stood in the doorway watching her walk the path back home. Liphee had talked non-stop. The fear she'd felt earlier that day had come close to paralyzing her and she knew that it was because she left Ginny in Kentucky and Peggy sick. Ivan eased some of the tension she'd carried home from work by assuring her that when she returned to Kentucky the following week Ginny and Peggy would both be waiting for her. No sooner than she left Ivan's door, Liphee was again overcome by the fear that'd plagued her all day. She started a load of laundry then she went upstairs to prepare a room for her sister and niece.

Mary sat in the front room staring at the screen on the television. Four times in the last twenty minutes she'd walked to the front door to peer out into the darkness, feeling the anticipation of something unknown. The kids had been restless all day and they went down for their nap that afternoon only to wake up cranky less than half of an hour later.

Three times that day she'd caught herself thinking of something that she wanted to tell George. Fresh tears appeared each time when she realized she would never talk to him again. Maggie remained on the bed in the front bedroom and at suppertime Mary carried a plate laden with food to her. An hour later, she carried the plate back to the kitchen, the food untouched. At eight-thirty Friday evening, Mary saw the dark forms of Ginny and Peggy approaching when she looked through the glass of the front door.

The two women and girl sat in the quiet room while the only interruption in the silence was the whoumpth... of the pilot light igniting the gas in the space heater. The temperature outside hovered at fifty degrees when Peggy led her mother into the night a few minutes later and the cool air felt good against her hot skin. Mary told her she needed to see a doctor. The pension check should arrive in the next day's mail and she should ask Eddie to take her to the doctor in the afternoon.

Ben was awake when Peggy closed the door and locked it for the night and he was sober. He'd been counting the hours all evening, hours that stood between him and tomorrow's bottle. Maybe the mail would run earlier tomorrow. In the last hour, his hands had grown clumsy holding the deck of cards and during the last game of solitaire he'd noticed the tremble in his fingers. He was bent over the cards displayed on the chair he'd brought in from the kitchen and Peggy turned down the volume on the television before

Across the Footbridge

saying goodnight. Ben never answered, just continued to turn the cards over from the pile in front of him. Two hours later, Peggy heard Roger come home. Her mother was in the bed with her and her father was in the bed across the room.

Exhaustion finally pulled Maggie into deep sleep for the first time in almost a week. She drifted towards the dark haven and back in time. Back through the years she went, past George and Jessie's deaths, past their births, back to the first night she and Charley slept together.

He walked up behind where she sat brushing her hair and his hand involuntarily moved to bury itself in the rich sheath of hair tumbling over her shoulders, falling almost to the floor. The color was something he'd never seen before, a mixture of all the autumn colors, layered on top of each other. As she brushed, the colors came into view one at a time.

"Mag, I've never seen anything as purty in all my life."

"I had four sisters Charley, each one purtier, or smarter, or better in one way or another. The only thing that my daddy ever said he liked about me was my hair. I've never cut it, an' I never will."

"Mag, I promise to do my best by you."

"You already have."

When she woke, her hand was tangled in the long gray tresses and tears had rolled down her cheeks to make wet spots on both sides of her pillow.

"Charley, please take care of our boys till I get there."

Liphee felt the coldness penetrating her bare legs as it worked its way under her skin and join with the fear that was flooding her body. Ginny was walking away from her and

241

when she ran to catch her, she caught sight of George in the distance and he was walking towards them. The people standing behind him clarified before her eyes. It was Pappy and he was holding Jesse. Ma was walking behind them with a bundle in her arms. Ginny was getting closer. Ma moved the top of the blanket to show Liphee what she was holding. She saw the color of the hair and then she knew. Ginny! No! Come back! No! No...

"Wake up!

She sat upright in bed, the overhead light illuminating the corners in the bedroom. John was standing at the side of the bed and his coat was still buttoned.

"Are you okay? I heard you screaming as soon as I opened the car door."

"We've gotta go get Ginny and Peggy!"

"We are, just as soon as she's well enough to travel."

...

He needed to tell her something. That was all that she could make out. She strained to listen, his voice fading as if he was walking away from her and she couldn't hear what he was saying. He was stuttering, like he did when he was excited about something.

"Slow down George, I can't understand what you're saying."

She watched as he took a deep breath before he opened his mouth again.

"I need to stop..."

Mary sat upright in bed. The children sleeping beside her didn't move when the sobs racked her body. "What

Across the Footbridge

George? What do you need to stop?"

She saw them waiting for her just as he had promised. They were all there and George was singing. She recognized the song; it was the one he used to sing to the kids when they had the colic. The man promised her that she could go when he returned. She'd be there soon. He walked in front of her as they made their way through the tunnel. He'd never let her go this far before and she longed to reach out and touch his hair. It was so white that it glowed in the darkness. She knew that it would be as soft as the clouds if only she could reach it. He heard the noise and turned around. No! She didn't want to go back. It was the noise; he made her go back because he heard the noise.

Roger smacked the top of the buzzing alarm clock.

Chapter Twenty-four

April 3, 1971

After the third ring an arm reached from beneath the covers with the second swipe of the hand removing the receiver from its cradle.

"Hmhhh... Hello,"

The clock on the nightstand described the urgency of the call with its glowing red numbers, *3:21 A.M.*

Norma turned to face the side of the bed where Ivan was sleeping seconds before. After thirty seconds of attentive listening, Ivan pulled the chain dangling from the lamp on the nightstand and pushed his feet towards the floor as light flooded the corner of the room.

"When? Oh God! Yes, of course I'll tell em."

"Old man, what is it? What's happened?"

He replaced the receiver and she could see it in his eyes when he turned to face her, a look that flooded her own body with fear. She knew he didn't want to answer, and knew that she wouldn't want to hear when he did. His face dropped into his upturned hands and the sound of his loud racking sobs penetrated the quiet.

. . .

Peggy opened her eyes against the bright light. The sockets of her eyes were sore and the corners crusty. The bed and room were empty and the house silent. How long had she been asleep...and where was her mother?

She heard him open the front door. He walked to the doorway and looked at the bed where she still lay.

"You need to get up and see to your mother."

He was dressed and clean-shaven and the usual tinge of red was missing from his eyes. He'd been awake for hours, shaving and changing his clothes before Roger left for work. He'd already made three trips up to the mailbox, each time taking Ginny with him. Hopefully, the mail would run soon cause he really needed a bottle.

Peggy sat on the edge of the bed, coaxing her body to move, the dampness around the base of her hair indicating that the fever was down. She moved from the bed to the kitchen and saw that the soup she hadn't been able to swallow the night before was still on the table, a thick skin covering the top. She dumped the soup in the trash and poured a dipper of water in the bowl. Her knees trembled under the weight of her body but she poured the rest of the water in a pan and set it at the back of the stove to heat. She carried the empty bucket to the front room.

"Daddy, could you bring in water before you go to town?"

He had the empty bucket in his hand when he saw the carrier moving slowly down the road, stopping at each mailbox. He filled the bucket from the spigot and carried it through the yard and into the house. Ben was waiting at the side of the road when the mail truck passed in front of him. He removed a brown envelope from his and Maggie's boxes and placed the one addressed to him in his pocket. He crossed the roads and tracks with Maggie's mail in his hand. He always took her check to the bank to cash with his.

Mrs. Tarrie was walking towards her mailbox when Ben walked away from his. Her cheeks were rouged and her house shoes were replaced with the ones that she wore to town. She'd been a widow for more than fifteen years. Twenty years before he died, her husband bought the land where her house stood and the ground behind, all the way down to the creek. He built their first house beside the stream and they lived in it till the kids were grown. One by one, the houses in front had been built to house one of their grown children and the last house built was the one where she lived. Instead of putting up another house for their youngest child, he built a new home for his wife. He died a year later. Her oldest son lived in one of the houses in the middle and his wife, whom he no longer lived with, now lived in the house by the creek. The other houses she rented out. Her house was the only one with indoor plumbing and the year before when the city ran water lines to her house, she had an outside spigot installed for the others. The old well would have to be filled in one of these days.

Ben left a few minutes later to go to the bank and the carryout across the bridge. Peggy poured the steaming water into the wash pan while keeping an eye on her mother's feet that were visible at the end of the bed in the next room. Ten minutes later she poured the dirty water down the drain and placed her dirty clothes on the heaping basket at the foot of her father's bed. Ginny hadn't moved since Ben left for town so Peggy dumped the basket, sorted the clothes into different piles and then put them back in the basket. She'd go to the laundromat the next day.

She felt the heat rising in her body before he returned and tried to drink some juice twice before giving up, her throat hurting with each swallow. She made a sandwich and poured milk in a glass for her mother before she lay across the bed. She struggled to keep her eyes open.

He stopped at Maggie's first, carrying her money in the same envelope he'd took in to her more than an hour before. He parked in front of the house a few minutes later, his hands steady on the gearshift. He let himself in the back door, feeling better than he had in a week. He'd thought about Berniece while he'd been driving across the bridge. He hadn't seen her since George's funeral. He wondered who she was chasing this week.

Ginny looked up when he entered the kitchen, looked at, not past him.

Across the Footbridge

"How're you feeling?"

...

Peggy knocked at the door twice before turning to go back home. Mrs. Tarrie called for a cab as soon as the mail arrived. She always went to town on check day. She did her banking and ate lunch at the counter at Murphy's, then walked to the A&P to buy her groceries. At two-ten the taxi stopped in front of her door. Twenty minutes later she was sitting in front of the television when Peggy knocked at her door again.

"Come in!"

Peggy realized where she'd been when she saw her pink cheeks and stockings rolled down to cover the swollen ankles. Peggy asked to use the phone and refused the offer of the dime store candy. Eddie answered on the third ring and told her that he'd be there in an hour to take her to the doctor.

Ben removed the bottle from behind the couch three times before Eddie turned into the drive leading to his parents' back door. The temperature outside was sixty degrees when Peggy walked outside to get in his car but the air felt cool against her feverish skin.

Eddie stopped the car a few feet from the front door. The street in front of the office was vacant and the sign on the door explained the deserted street. The office was closed till Monday.

Dr. Bentley had taken care of Peggy since she was small. He'd come to America after the last World War and his waiting room remained empty for the first year. Gradually his practice grew. His first patients were people desperate for medical attention and his door had been open during the late hours that the other doctors closed theirs to go home to their families.   Each new patient returned, most of them recommending him to someone else. He took few vacations and his office hours were long. He never made appointments and he called his patients back to the examining room himself, always taking a sick child back before someone waiting to complain about a minor ailment. He based his fees on the appearances of his patients and a twenty-dollar office visit could be reduced to three if he thought he was removing grocery money from a father's wallet.

Eddie and Peggy returned to the car.

"Do you want to go to the Emergency Room?"

"Nah, I can wait till Monday."

Eddie stopped at the drug store at the edge of town. He returned to the car with all the over the counter medicines he could find to reduce a fever and sooth a sore throat.   He stopped at a drive-in and ordered a hamburger and milkshake. Peggy managed to swallow one bite of the sandwich and most of the shake. When he let her out in front of the house, he told her that he'd be back on Monday to take her to the doctor.

. . .

"Why don't you try a little?

He held the opened bottle in front of her three times before she spoke.

"Ben I can't! Don't make me do it! I can't, I'm sick!"

. . .

Mary saw her face through the glass and she opened the door and looked past her shoulder for Ben.

"Ginny, are you by yourself?"

"Mary he wants me to be a wife to him an' I can't!"

Already shocked to see her alone, Ginny's coherent words startled her more.

"Whatta you mean… he wants you to be a wife to him?"

"Ben…he wants me to be a wife to him!"

"Its okay, just come in and sit down. You can stay here till Peggy gets back from the doctor."

Ben knocked at the door he'd opened and entered earlier that day. He found his wife sitting on the couch beside her sister and saw the tears still glistening on Ginny's cheeks. He also saw the anger in Mary's eyes.

The words exchanged between them could be heard in the next yard but Ginny was removed from it all, unaware of the conversation that was taking place around her. Ben was leading her back across the tracks when Peggy let herself in the house.

Ben drained the last drop from the jug at five-thirty. Roger was turning into the driveway when he passed his father going out.

…

"Are you sure you don't want me to stay home tonight?"

"I'm sure. I'll take her over to Grandma's with me when I go. I want to go to bed early anyway."

Roger passed his father in the driveway again. Ben had fought the Friday evening traffic on the bridge then stopped for takeout chicken in town before turning towards home. He broke the seal on the jug of wine before he left the parking lot of the carryout store. He parked the truck, slipped an unopened pint into his pocket and placed the jug behind the

Across the Footbridge

front seat. He carried the bucket of chicken into the empty house.

. . .

Larry had been quiet since they returned home from the funeral. He and Sally went to her parent's house early that afternoon and when her brother reached into the drawer for a deck of cards, she knew that it would be a while before she'd be going home. Larry sat down at the kitchen table and she found a book and a quiet corner in another room. It was almost midnight when he carried their sleeping son towards the car. Twenty minutes later, he placed the baby in the crib and Sally turned out the lights.

Eddie dropped Peggy at home and drove past the poolroom to see if maybe a game was in progress. At seven-thirty, when Roger stopped by the store to buy a pack of gum, Eddie was still there. The brothers played one game of pool before they both left the building. Eddie pointed his car in the direction of home and Roger headed his towards the bridge.

. . .

Peggy led Ginny across the roads and tracks a little past nine. Ben was passed out on the couch when she locked the front door. Peggy took the cough syrup and decongestant with the aspirin before crawling in beside her mother, the bulb in the ceiling of the kitchen lighting the path between the two beds.

"Goodnight Mommy."

Peggy fell asleep with her right hand clutching the material of the shirt that her mother slept in.

. . .

Across the Footbridge

The opening of the kitchen door was what woke her and she saw his reflection in the mirror on the dresser. Then, Peggy's eyes took in the empty space on the other side of the bed. Ben closed the door and stood looking down at her.

"Where's my Mommy?"

He never answered, but walked past the bed and through the doorway into the other room. Peggy grabbed the pants she'd taken off an hour before and pulled her coat on over her bare breasts before she ran out into the night.

Mary had turned out the lights minutes before and Peggy's pounding on the front door woke Maggie and two of the kids.

It was ten-thirty when the phone in Eddie's dining room rang. Seconds later Becky stood in the doorway watching the tail lights till they disappeared. She closed the door and went to the phone.

"Mom, can you come get the boys?"

...

The dispatcher who took the call wasn't sure if it would be city or county. The address that the neighbor gave him was two blocks from the jurisdiction line so he sent a car from both precincts just to keep his butt covered. The first patrol car arrived the same time as Eddie. Several of the neighbors had already formed one search party.

...

"Mam, did you hear anything out of the ordinary tonight?"

Her robe was pulled tight around her short stout body. She removed her dentures and placed the silk cap over her hair about ten-twenty, she told the officer. That's when she heard the voices outside the house, while she was in the bathroom. But she couldn't make out anything that had been said.

"Are there any open wells or culverts on the property?"

"There's not any culverts that I know of an' I had the lid on the well nailed shut, just in case something like this would happen."

The lights from the police cars brought out a few more of the neighbors. Spotlights were aimed into the dark murky water of the creek. Eddie left in his car driving towards the old neighborhood. She'd been seen heading up that way another time that she disappeared. One of the neighbors left with an officer and a spotlight to check the tunnel where the road crossed over the tracks.

Mary and Peggy were looking in the growth of high weeds behind the outhouse when the noise from the radio caught their attention. The window on the driver's side was rolled down, the sounds of the Grand Ole Opry penetrating the night air.

"Ben, ain't you gonna help us look for Ginny?"

"Right now I'm gonna eat my chicken and listen to my radio."

"Come on, Peggy. Somebody said that they thought they saw her about daybreak the other day walking up Dixon hill. Let's walk up that way!"

Peggy and Mary were at the corner of the road that led to the store when a car came to a stop. Eddie leaned across the seat and rolled down the passenger window.

"You'd better come on back, they think they've found her. My Daddy thinks that she's in the well!"

Hands pulled her away from the crowd that'd gathered around the well and someone pushed her into the front seat of a car. The rotating lights moved through the windshield, illuminating the interior, then dropping her back into darkness. The glare of approaching headlights brought her momentarily back to reality. Roger was home.

"Oh my God! Somebody get to Roger!"

One of the neighbors and his wife were each holding one side of her but the man left the car to go place his arms around her brother as his screams penetrated the dark curtain that was closing in around her. The woman buried Peggy in her arms as Roger cried out into the night for his mother.

...

"Somebody'd better have the dispatcher give the coroner a call...and tell em to cancel the diver. I think we've found her...an' see if some of the family can come over here and identify the body. Better make sure she's the one we've been looking for!"

The men's faces were captured and frozen for a split second with each rotation of the blue and white lights.

...

Larry padded barefoot down the hall and picked the receiver up on the fourth ring.

Twenty-eight years later,

From out of the ashes,

The ringing of the phone pierced the blanket of sleep and while my husband pulled himself from the warm security of our bed, my conscious mind reached out in an attempt to alert me to the time. My eyes remained closed when he picked up the receiver in the kitchen, relief flooding my body when his voice remained calm.

"Yes, she's here…you read the manuscript? What did you think? Do you want to talk to her?"

Terror surged through me, awakening nerve endings in its path and I tasted the old fear when it reached my mouth. My body fought opposite urges, one force pulling me deeper into the bed, the other pushing me towards a voice that was waiting for me.

"Hello.. are you still speaking to me?" the first sentence spoken to my brother after he read the words that I wrote about our mother.

"Yes, an' I called to thank you."

Relief flooded the path that seconds before fear had blazed and my body responded to the relief, tears seeping from the corners of my eyes.

"Tell me that this isn't a dream."

Months of pent-up tension slowly ebbed from my body as a shell of protection that we'd placed around our hearts cracked and the ancient wall started to collapse. Phone wires stretched the distance of miles as our hearts reached out, closing in the gap that pain had made twenty-seven years before.

Our mother died twenty-seven years, seven months, and five days before and it took that many years, months, and days for her children to begin to accept and understand, then start to let go. The manuscript was the key that unlocked the last door and the walls that we constructed around our hearts had stood more than a quarter of a century.

. . .

With the writing of my words, I retraced the steps that led my mother to her death. Each step brought pain and suppressed memories resurrected from deep within me. Each page also brought me a step closer to an understanding of what happened, and answered some of the *whys*. With this, an acceptance started to grow in my heart, my first step towards healing. My brother, Larry, called me in the middle of this

Across the Footbridge

night to tell me that he would walk at my side, as we walked away from the mother that we buried so many years before, and this time our hearts will be filled with the love that we will continue to carry, love that was her legacy to her children.

At the age of forty-three I went back in time to visit the years that I spent with my mother. I made this journey as a woman, and as a mother. For years I had viewed my childhood through the eyes of a child but when I walked the road a second time, I saw things along the sides that had previously escaped me. Without the discomfort of hunger, I could see the pain that was present in my mother's eyes the days that she had little or no food to feed her children. There are recollections of hands that bled from the irritation of the cold wind on them as they hung our clothes on an outside line to be brought inside hours later frozen into stiff forms. My mother suffered the pain of poverty twice. She suffered in the life that she lived, and again as she acknowledged the needs of her children, needs that she couldn't always meet. She eventually succumbed to the impossible odds that life placed her against, but through all of this, she loved us. She instilled into each of her children respect for her and my father, respect for others, and the strength to break the cycle of poverty.

The sand in the hourglass trickled away our time with her, the particles representing time that we were losing as our youths vanished. We struggled with the force that was striving to remove her from us and we lost the battle, with the horrible disease making the ultimate claim on her life. It left us defeated, and motherless.

Four children walked away from her grave, each

257

holding to his or her heart a last memory of their mother and these memories we embraced as shields, refusing to release our last images of her. As we harbored the pain that'd become our identification with her, we allowed the monster in her life to achieve another victory. It removed her from us, leaving memories of pain and death in the spaces of our hearts that we held in reserve for her.

Years passed with our memories hoarded deep within our hearts, as a last piece of Christmas is hidden away in a child's room. It was the last of something a person refuses to share with the knowledge that once it is gone, it can never be replaced. Half a lifetime later, I stumbled onto the key that unlocked the door to the space in my heart where my mother still lives. With this discovery, I would in turn show my brothers the way out of the hell that claimed our mother as its prisoner. We won the final battle when the monster lost its power to remove her from our hearts.

We buried her at the top of a little hill and in the summertime a gentle breeze blows over her. The fears that she endured while here with us are no more and the love that she left with her children will heal and nurture us now as she nurtured us so many years ago.

...

Today, 2.5 million Americans suffer from Schizophrenia. The disease that haunted Ginny's life for two generations, still has no known cure. More prevalent than Alzheimer's, insulin-dependent diabetes, multiple sclerosis, or muscular dystrophy, Schizophrenia costs the United States $33 billion annually.

Across the Footbridge
Schizophrenia is a biological illness characterized by abnormalities in brain structure and chemistry and it is influenced by environmental factors. Today, the combinations of drug therapy along with counseling that assists the patient in identifying symptoms of the disease and help with management of stress have greatly improved many schizophrenics' lifestyles.

People with schizophrenia, particular those under the age of 55, have a mortality rate eight times higher than those who do not have it. One quarter to one half of schizophrenic individuals attempt suicide, *one in ten succeeds*.

After thirty years, where are they now?
The leftovers from the party are still on the counter when Roger makes his way towards the front door, and passing displays of advertisement for the new management, he locks the front door for the last time. It's his last day here. Thirty years have passed and he secures the building that took him from a boy into middle age, for the last time.

He hired in to wash shirts, the lowest paying job in the business. Both of his brothers started here, then moved on to other jobs. He was barely sixteen when he reported for his first day of training and the heat was the first thing that he noticed.

The training consisted of a finger pointing. "You wash those shirts in that machine and you dry them in that machine and then you give them to her!" 'Her' was the person that operated the shirt presser.

He didn't see his boss again till he was handed his paycheck at the end of the second week and by then he'd adjusted to the heat. It took less effort to adjust to the paycheck that arrived each Friday. He purchased an old car and within a few weeks he'd acquired the necessary skills to persuade the old washers and dryers to perform on a regular basis. The woman who pressed the shirts became a smiling face that greeted him six mornings a week as he became familiar with the machinery and the people where he spent his days. The old presses hissed at him when he passed them on his way to pick up or deliver shirts at the front of the store.

After a few months he was promoted to the dry-cleaning machine and another person in need of a job took over his discarded duties. He bought a few new clothes and a nicer car. He lost his shyness around the other employees when they started to call for him instead of the boss if they had problems with their presses. In time, he learned the personalities of the equipment and the operators, all of which were older than he was.

He'd been there less than a year when he took financial responsibility for his mother and sister for most of one winter. He paid rent and bought food for three on an income that was stretched to cover the needs of one. He was nineteen when his mother died and his co-workers became part of his family in the months that followed.

His sister moved north after their mother died and he and his father moved into a little house at the outskirts of town. Before he was twenty-one his father was placed beside his mother and for the first time in his life he was alone.

The woman the boss hired to take in and hand out the shirts and dry-cleaning was almost twice his age. He watched her from behind the old presses that demanded more and more of his time and soon he found more reasons to go to the front where she spent her days. He learned that she was divorced and the mother of three children and that she wasn't interested in dating. If she had an interest, it certainly wouldn't have been with him. She could possibly be his mother. His mother never looked like she did, and granted, he had loved his mother dearly, but she'd never stirred the kind of feelings in him that this woman did.

She refused to see him socially so he started appearing on her front porch in the evenings. He became better aquatinted with her and her children started to look forward to his evening visits. At bedtime, she left him sitting on the front porch when she went inside for the night. Winter arrived, and she asked him not to come by anymore. She couldn't have him sitting outside in the cold night air. The next evening she found him sitting in his usual spot and she asked him in. They were married a few months later.

They went to and from work together every day for the next twenty years. They bought the house where they lived and he refurbished it and put in a swimming pool in the back yard. He stood at her side at each of her children's weddings. The years passed and he assumed more responsibility of the business. He couldn't recall the exact time that he took over the management of it. He returned to school and finished his education.

He built a new house on some acreage in the country they'd discovered a few years back. He designed the house himself and built it in the hours that he stole from the evenings that he could have been relaxing. He hauled most of the materials up the side of a mountain in the back of his pickup.

Across the Footbridge

He often wondered why he was moving so far from town, till he got there, experienced the quietness, and the view. He could see for miles in all directions and at nightfall only the sounds of nature were heard. After five years it was almost completed and they moved from the house in town to the top of a mountain. Each day she sat beside him on the trip to town and back.

He grew tired of twenty-hour days, enthusiasm for the completion of his home worn away. His boss wanted to sell him the business but all he wanted was a little time to rest. For the last few years he'd surrendered his Sunday mornings to the business and it'd been years since he and his wife had been away from home for the night. She retired this year and he started going into town alone.

He'd wanted to make a change for quite a while. Each time he mentioned leaving, the amount of his next paycheck had increased. The man who taught him to wash shirts so many years before had turned his business over to him and no one seemed to understand. It wasn't more money that he wanted, not more responsibility he craved. He just wanted a little time before it was too late. He'd spent thirty years of his life here. How many years did he have left?

He thought of the dream home he'd soon return to and that it contained all of the modern conveniences that were missing from his boyhood home. It seemed as if it was only yesterday that he carried in coal and water for his mother. Now, his brother's and sister's children had little ones of their own. How had decades passed? His wife's retirement had alerted him to the passing of his youth and without her at his side when he made the long drive to and from work, he'd finally had time to look at his life.

The restlessness that he'd covered up for so many years had room to emerge from within him and he realized that he'd been left standing at the side of the road somewhere in his past. He bought an old dump truck a few months back. It was an investment in his future, an investment in his relationship with his wife. The best hours of his life were spent in her company. The last few months he'd left her at home when he went to his job that now held no meaning and he returned to her late in the evening to repeat the process the following day. For the first time in more than twenty years, he was lonely. He spent long hours of the nights repairing the truck that would soon replace the business. He would take control of his life, with his wife and best friend once again at his side.

He dreamed of having time to do the things that he wanted to do. His house was still almost completed and the yard needed landscaping. His wife needed him at her side and he needed to be there. It was those needs that gave him the courage to finally leave his mistress, the job that'd consumed thirty years of his life.

A large corporation had purchased the building and contents, leaving the other twenty-five employees facing the unknown and when the man who'd signed his checks realized that he was really leaving, he decided to go too. Would his friends still have jobs after the ownership was transferred? Would they still want those jobs? The needs that the man identified with almost forced him to remain. He'd lived most of his forty-six years for others' needs.

The party was filled with tears and well wishes. He

knew each face and piece of equipment that he was leaving as a mother knows a child borne of her own body. He stood strong and proud as each person hugged him, wished him well and walked into a future that he had disrupted.

He left the front area and walked the distance to his small office. This room reminded him of his life, too many things squeezed into too small of a space. He removed his personal items yesterday, the remainder would become the property of the new owner. He placed his keys on the desk and walked out the door. The last of the day's steam hissed at him when he passed, the last time that he'd hear the noises of the building settling in for its night of sleep. He turned out lights, running his hand across machinery as familiar to him as his wife's face. He pulled the back door shut and walked slowly towards the person waiting in the parking lot.

His leaving here was similar to his beginning. He felt excitement for something unknown and he felt a little fear. This time, he drew comfort from the hand that reached out to him, the hand of his wife. With a shrug of his shoulders he released the burden that'd tied him to his mistress then started the engine of his truck and headed it in the direction of the highest peak. He would deal with his future tomorrow. Tonight, he wanted to spend a little time with his wife.

Turn around, turn around,

They built the new refinery about five miles out past the city limits. The lights are visible at night from Roger's yard. Eddie turned onto the highway that ran past the bottom of the hill where his brother lived. He could remember when the streets had all ran parallel with the river and in the last twenty years the city had stretched to encompass the area where he used to hunt squirrels. The last city traffic light was now ten miles from the entrance to the bridge instead of three.

His usual stop netted him a bag of takeout food and a friendly smile held in reserve for the regular late night customers. He cut the power to the engine at the top of the hill and braked to a stop at the second driveway then let himself in the door of the house that was now paid for. The last mortgage payment was mailed two months before. The house was still the same size, having stretched through the years to accommodate three growing children. The second bedroom now held the remnants of the material that Becky converted into quilts. He'd remodeled the interior several times, put up a fence in the back yard and later took it down.

The first ten years had been rough. Those first years his take-home pay barely covered the expenses of a new house, new furniture, and new lifestyle. The kids had grown along with his income. He remembered the first new vehicle he'd driven off the lot, recalling the years that he'd dreaded going home to face Becky. He never knew how to tell her about the pain that he carried in his heart. He struggled, she suffered, and eventually time did the job for him. The years actually put enough distance between his childhood, his months in Nam, and his mother's death to allow him to show her how much he really did love her. He couldn't ever go back and change those first years but he could make the rest of their time together different.

The small golf clubs on the couch told of a visitor that he'd missed. He was sharing his passion for golf with his grandson and shared his passion for fishing with his two grown sons. He'd walked his daughter down the aisle, her gown billowing out in front of them. He had been given a second chance. This time he spent time with his grandchildren that he missed from his own children's lives, searching the toy aisles and ice-cream parlors for the something special that only Papaw could provide. The diamonds he slipped into his wife's un-expectant hands always reminded him of the sparkle that was in her eyes the first time he saw her. His years of returning home late, being quiet, filled with pain, are now replaced with years of home improvements and late calls to the all-night pizza delivery. Sometimes, his granddaughter has a craving in the middle of the night.

He shares the contents of the bag with Becky while she fills him in on the daily activities of the kids that return home at least once a day. He talks of their trip to the coast next month and she tells him that his sister called. The last of Ginny and Ben's grandchildren will be married in a few months.

Fried Egg Sandwiches,

Three men stood under the shade of a maple tree and waited for the last of the procession to pass. With the dust still resettling in the ruts of the dirt road, they picked up the shovels that 'd been leaning against the tree and slowly move towards the last pile of dirt of the day. The men had dug three holes and put the dirt back on two of the three fresh graves in the cemetery that day. In the heat of a late August afternoon, three shovels were placed on hooks and the door closed on the shed at the back of the cemetery. The silence of the past hour was relieved when they exited the gates.

Across the Footbridge

Once the cemetery faded from their view, the men picked up the conversation from lunch as if the last four hours hadn't existed. The turmoil, the creator of the silence was a daily event in their lives as thoughts of the families that they were going home to mingled with memories of the day's grieving families, the livelihood of their employment.

The road ended at an intersection and the men parted with the waves of tired arms. Two men walked east and one turned west. The lone gravedigger had held a pick or shovel in his hands for more years than he cared to recall and he preferred the pick to the shovel. The pride he associated with being a miner would never become a part of the man who shoveled dirt onto the tops of caskets. The shovel just enabled him to feed his family. He was anticipating the opening of another mineshaft when he would turn his shovel over to more willing hands. It was a five-minute walk from the intersection to the small red house that he was approaching.

The shade of a wooden footbridge shelters the little girl sitting on the bank of the creek. She peers into a hole that just swallowed a crawdad, oblivious to the cool mud oozing up between her toes. She senses the vibration of the bridge as she hears the footsteps and the crawdad is forgotten. Her daddy's home!

Peggy Ann is at the end of the bridge before he is and the reach of two hands becomes one motion as her hand is swallowed inside the callused one. The burning ache between his shoulder blades vanishes as he looks down at the top of the small head, his little girl.

They stop at the steps leading to the front porch where she tells him that she's been good. He tells her a surprise should be hers for the effort and opens his lunch pail, looking inside for something that might be hers. With just the right amount of hesitation, he removes it from the box. Wrapped in wax paper is the fried egg sandwich that is part of their daily ritual.

Years pass, and on a cold February day she walks away from her daddy. Two men wait for her to disappear from their sight and when her back is no longer visible, they pick up the shovels and walk towards the mound of dirt. Peggy walked away from her father and away from the little girl who waited by the bridge.

...

A lifetime later,

The old man feels as helpless as he did years before while waiting out the hours of labor that his wife endured giving birth to his children. Years became decades with the swiftness of months becoming years. Now, he's retired, his wife gone, and his children are all adults. His body tells him that it's time to rest but in his heart he knows that he will have all of eternity to rest. What can he do now? The retired shoe salesman sits alone in a quiet room, and he waits. He thinks of his wife as he tries to make sense of passing years that come from endless days. Where did it all go?

Lying on a table beside his chair, are pages of another person's life and the stories that he reads introduce him to a little girl who lived a lifetime ago, *a little girl that he calls Kitty.*

Peggy was eighteen years old when she walked away from her father's grave, leaving her mother and father to face eternity together. She moved to another state and established a new life. She married and gave birth to the next generation and she found her mother in the shape of her daughter's eyes, and saw gentleness from her father recreated in her son. She felt sadness for two children who would never know the love of two grandparents.

Years put distance between the little girl she'd been and the woman Peggy became while the void in her heart became a holding place for the memories that she never had the chance to make. When her children were born, she felt a void of missing rejoicing and with first teeth and steps, she knew that there was one element missing. At times she grew tired of the sometimes, overwhelming responsibilities of being a parent. A shoulder for her to rest her burden on was missing and Peggy missed the sharing of the events that led her children into adulthood.

A divorce and the struggles of bringing up two children alone filled the space of time and Peggy came to accept that she'd never experience the unconditional love of a parent again. The security of that love was buried in her past with picks, shovels, and fried egg sandwiches. She learned to discipline herself in times of uncertainty and praise herself for jobs well done.

Two worlds from the past merged the day that the retired shoe salesman met the little girl who once played under a bridge. She found in him the gentle love of a father and he saw in her reminders of a daughter that was no longer with him. He looked on as his son and Peggy were joined in marriage and the same vows that united Peggy and his son reunited two hearts of yesterday.

Through the years that followed he watched as life continued to place obstacles in front of Peggy and he felt helpless in his desire to eliminate her pain because he wanted to shelter her heart from any future grief. He was introduced to the little girl who played under the bridge in the pages of her writing that Peggy shared with him. He could see where she had been and Peggy wanted him to see where she was going, to see that she was growing.

One day, not so very long ago, he called her on the phone. He heard happiness in her voice and she heard parental pride in his. He wanted to share some of her writings with his friends and she agreed to his request and returned to her typewriter.

How would she ever tell him? She wished for the ability to place her feelings in a glass bottle because she wanted him to see the wonder of it all. She wanted to tell him that she understood. He can't replace yesterday, but he is a part of who she will become tomorrow.

Where are they now?

Maggie suffered a stroke three weeks after Ginny's death and remained bedridden until her death in the fall of 1974. Ben died on Valentine's Day, 1972. Mary's children are grown and she has eight grandchildren at this writing. Liphee is living in Indiana. Her health is in a decline and she maintains a small home next door to her son. She has two grandchildren. Peggy and Larry both live in Indiana, separated by a distance of fourteen miles.

All of Ginny's and Ben's grandchildren graduated from high school and the majority of them from college.